BODY REVIVAL

WORKBOOK

BODY REVIVAL WORKBOOK

Cover Design by Graphic Designer Kris Voelker
Edited by Deb McGowan
Compiled by Jennifer Rohner
Formatted for print by Shanda Trofe

For permission requests, write to the publisher:
SDJ Productions
4640 W. Redfield Road
Glendale, AZ 85306

www.sunnydawnjohnston.com

ISBN-13: 978-0-9798119-7-5

Printed in the United States of America.

BODY REVIVAL
WORKBOOK

SUNNY DAWN JOHNSTON

This Workbook is dedicated to the light and love within us all.

Thank you for your willingness to show up and look beyond the physical manifestations of the body to the emotional reasons they have manifested in the first place. As you grow, expand, and heal … you will automatically show others new ways to heal as well.

This Body Revival Workbook is an interactive experiential process designed to lead you to greater health, wellness and a higher vibration of being and LIVING.

Your "inner-work" will bring you the clarity, compassion and commitment that you have longed for. Your Body, Mind, Spirit and Emotions will thank you for the journey.

Thank you for sharing and shining your unique light in the world.

Sunny Dawn Johnston

CONTENTS

Introduction...iii

Before We Get Started...ix

Day 1: The Mind-Body Connection (It Really IS That Big of a Deal...)................1

Day 2: You and Your Body: Best Friends FOREVER 11

Day 3: Move to the Music: Mind, Body, AND Spirit Jams 21

Day 4: Maintaining Your Own Energy 27

Day 5: Do You "Measure Up"? (Comparison, Rulers, and Other Torturous Things)............37

Day 6: Vibrational Eating: Bringing the Love to Your Food............................45

Day 7: Stretch: It's Not JUST for Your Body 55

Day 8: The Many Masks We Wear (and How to Let Them Go).........................61

Day 9: One Breath at a Time..69

Day 10: Nobody Does This Alone: Asking for Help..75

Day 11: Time for a New (Body) Story?...85

Day 12: Decoding the Language of Your Body 95

Day 13: Let It Flow: The Power and Magic of Water 105

Day 14: Functionality Over Physicality (How It Works vs. How It Looks)............113

Day 15: Let's Move! Putting the BODY in Mind-Body-Spirit...........................123

Day 16: Pictures and Perspective 131

Day 17: Decluttering the Clutter ("Real" and Imagined) 147

Day 18: Agreements, Contracts, and Vows: Are They Serving You Anymore?................159

Day 19: Beauty Sleep – Healing Your BFF Through Rest...............................169

Day 20: A "Touchy" Subject (The Importance of Physical Connection)..................................179

Day 21: Change Your Habits, Change Your Experience..187

Day 22: Be Affirmative. Be Complimentary ... to Yourself and the WORLD 195

Conclusion 203

About the Author...205

Other Books, Products, and Services by Sunny Dawn Johnston................................207

INTRODUCTION

FORGET EVERYTHING YOU THOUGHT YOU KNEW ABOUT YOUR BODY BECAUSE IT'S ALL ABOUT TO CHANGE.

(Or should I say it's about to be revived?)

Body Revival. What does that sound like to you? My team and I took a little while longer than we thought to come up with the name for this experience. But we waited for the right one. After all, it was important that the name we landed on had the right energy to it. Why?

Because this book was not going to sound like just any other "get your body back" or "shape up for the New Year" program. I didn't want it to sound like everything and everyone else out there. This book, this program, and this movement is different. And I think you're going to see that pretty fast.

Why "revival," though? Because this program isn't about getting to a number on the scale or a clothing size that you're sure will solve all of your inner pain. It's not about eating this and not eating that. It's definitely not about the world's most badass fat-burning fitness routine either. (Believe it or not, I've never been much of a gym rat or an aerobics queen. Far from it, if you really want to know the truth!)

It's a body revival because it's about taking your power back. Pulling in your energy and bringing yourself back to yourself. Retrieving your energy back from the people, choices, and experiences that might've pulled it away from you.

We're talking about getting your inner being back. Making sure that the beliefs, thoughts, and bullshit you might've gathered over the years relinquishes its power over you. It's about taking your power back from a conscious and present place.

THAT is what I mean by "Body Revival."

And you know what? Being a part of this movement makes you a revivalist! Now, that might sound a little bit strange to you, and maybe it even brings up some negative connotations and stereotypic images. But all that "revival" means is that you're taking yourself, your power, and your life back to where it belongs: with YOU.

This program is all about reawakening the Mind, Body, and Spirit connection that is your very nature. And I promise that it's not going to be like any diet or exercise book of the week that you've ever read.

I bet that's great news, isn't it?

Now, I want to be clear on a few things before we jump in. I'm not a doctor. I am not a nutritionist or a physical therapist. I'm not a personal trainer, nor do I have a college degree. I'm not here to give you scientifically proven information. If that's what you're looking for, fair enough. There are plenty of options out there for that. I might not be your person.

But what I AM here to offer you is true, honest-to-God LIFE experience. Twenty years of working with other people. Thirty plus years of slogging through my own body issues, body shaming, bouts with disease, and weight issues. Not to mention finding body acceptance, body joy, and body love in the process.

So, if you're interested in hearing a new spin on an old topic, this is the place for you. If you're ready to make some big expansions in your awareness, your insight, and your mindset, stay with me. If you're ready to make new choices, commit to your own self-care, and actually start loving the skin that you're in, then you're ready for a real revival.

It's not just about what you eat or how you work out. It's about loving your body as if it were your best friend. It's about committing to your own self-love, and meaning it this time.

When you truly connect your Mind, Body, and Spirit, and you realize that for best results the three must work together, your whole life can change.

Or should I say that it will "revive"?

But it's all about making that Mind, Body and Spirit connection CONSISTENTLY.

Because if there's no consistent action, there won't be any consistent results. That's true of pretty much everything.

If you're not familiar with my story, let me tell you a little bit about how I got here. How I got to this whole Body Revival journey? I've lived it. I didn't go to school to learn about it. It didn't just read about it in a book and then share it. It's a journey I've walked personally, and it's been going on for over 40 years now.

And let me tell you, it hasn't always been pretty. In fact, it's been a battle.

When I was first born, the nurses wrote the word "battle" on my mother's chart. This is how I came into this world – through a battle. So, was I doomed to fight myself for my entire life? Well, it hasn't exactly been a struggle my entire life. The first 10 – 12 years I felt in alignment for the most part with my internal world. Most of the time, I knew who I was on the inside. The "battle" part came into play around the age of 13, when I realized that the version of me who showed up on the outside didn't fit who I knew I was on the inside. Whether it was my personality, the way I carried myself through the world, or my physical appearance, what I had felt inside and what I experienced outside didn't quite match up.

Then as my body started changing, it began to grab my attention. The more weight I gained, the more it got my attention. The more I created illnesses and diseases within my body, the more it got my attention.

What was happening? My body was simply trying to tell me something. It was trying to tell me the places where I had fallen out of alignment with my mind and Spirit. It was giving me all the messages I could've possibly needed in the form of weight gain, weight loss, diseases and health issues.

If only I would've been able to see them, though!

But at the time, I didn't want to see. I didn't want to know the root of all my pain, suffering, and self-loathing. I wanted an easy fix. Take a pill and lose 10 pounds. Exercise like this and eat like that and be a perfect size whatever. I wanted to push the "easy" button. But that wasn't going to happen.

Then everything got a lot worse. First, it started with weight issues. Then the diseases started showing up. Then I got pregnant and nearly died giving birth. I contracted a parasite that stuck with me for 4 years. I was diagnosed with osteopenia. And in the midst of all that madness, I lost three babies.

My body just kept disappointing me over and over again. It was to the point where I hated my body. And believe me, that's not a word I use very often. But I truly hated my body.

But here's the shocker: what I eventually started to realize was that through all that I put my body through – the pressure, the self-deprecation, the anger, and the blame – it still kept showing up for me. My heart kept beating and my lungs kept breathing. I could still move through life even when I was at my worst. No matter what I did – even almost dying once – it just kept coming through for me.

What I learned was that my body had always been my very best friend. And I was a really shitty friend right back. Of course, my only defense was that I didn't know that my body and I were friends. I kind of thought we were enemies.

So, no wonder I kept having the same kind of experiences! I was bringing a lot of pain into my body. And when energy enters the body as pain, it's going to come out through pain. But when you start releasing those hurtful emotions, the pain that you feel when they leave is going to be a lot less than the pain you've been carrying with you for so long. That I can personally attest to.

Trust me, I get it. I've had disease. I've healed disease. I've had weight issues, and I've healed them, too. I've been through the eating disorders, the body shame, the bullshit stories and the ugliness. I could recall that pain in a heartbeat if I had to.

But you know what comes up for me now? Gratitude.

Now I feel such gratitude for this amazing body. I have so much appreciation for the journey that I've taken, no matter how scathing it has been. I've learned, grown, and expanded. And now I have the privilege of sharing that journey with you. And I sincerely hope you'll join me on this journey of gratitude.

So, what does Body Revival entail, and how are we going to get started?

The very first thing I'd like you to do is to set an intention for these 22 days. You're going to need this book, an additional journal, a pen, and an open heart. I want you to write down your intentions for the next 22 days. What do you really wish to get out of Body Revival, and what is that intention right now?

You see, a lot of us don't live life intentionally, but rather, reactively. And if you don't have an intention, you don't have direction. The Universe, Spirit, or God won't have any way to direct it. Let's start off with an intention. Ask yourself what you would like to see, experience, feel, and know over the next 22 days.

Once you've set your intentions, what happens next?

Here's how it's going to go down: every day for 22 days, you're going to start the day with appreciation. You're going to take five minutes every day to write in this workbook (or your own personal journal, if you prefer) your appreciation for your body and everything it does for you. Choose one thing that you love about your body each day, then take five minutes to journal about what you truly love about your body.

Now, I'm not saying that you have to bullshit yourself. Sometimes, you'll have days where the only thing that you appreciate about your body is that you're still breathing. On a great day, on the other hand, you might feel confident, sexy, and ready to kick ass and take names. Either way, it's OK. The point is to get into a consistent practice of appreciating your body and doing it sincerely in the moment.

So, every day will start out with five minutes of appreciation journaling. Then you'll receive a different exercise every day with homework and worksheets to help keep you focused and consistent.

I'm not gonna lie. Some of this will stretch you way beyond your comfort zone. It might make you feel uncomfortable. There might even be considerable pain. But like I said, the pain that you feel when you let the pain out of your body pales in comparison to how much pain you feel when it's still living in there.

You might believe that you've "already done this" and you might feel resentful of having to face it again. But let me tell you this: I don't want you to negate the work you've already done. I'm not saying that you haven't done any work. It's just that in doing the work, you've revealed another layer. Different challenges come up with different layers as we're ready to heal them. So, if you're here today and you're showing up with the presence of mind and the desire to change, then you're ready.

But don't feel overwhelmed by the layers. Feel excited about the opportunity to move through them. Be grateful that you're at the point where you have the ability to do it, and give yourself all the credit that you deserve for that. I'm telling you to feel grateful as you go through the journey. Feel as much appreciation as you can in every moment that you're in. Because it is a journey of appreciation and gratitude.

So once again, let me ask you this: are you ready to go on the journey with me from wherever you are right now to genuine, loving, full appreciation of your body? Because believe it or not, my friend, this body is the perfect vehicle for your Spirit in this lifetime. That's why you chose this body. And your body can be your best friend…if you're willing to recognize it as such.

Once you make friends with your body and re-engage it with your mind and Spirit, your body will respond. And it's going to respond in amazing ways. That I can personally attest to. And that's what I want for you.

Are you ready?

LET'S DO THIS!

BEFORE WE GET STARTED...

Take a moment, take a deep breath, and feel into where you are.

Ask yourself this: *What is my intention for the next 22 days? How do I want to feel, what do I want to experience, and what do I want to learn?*

Write down everything that you want to get out of this 22-day journey. What are your hopes, your aspirations, and your intentions as we go through each day together?

Take five to 10 minutes and see what comes up for you. Feel free to write it all down right here or in your personal journal.

_____

_____

_____

_____

_____

_____

_____

_____

_____

DAY 1: THE MIND-BODY CONNECTION (IT REALLY IS THAT BIG OF A DEAL...)

If you've read one of my books or taken one of my courses before, you know that I like to jump in and get started quickly. Most of the time I like to jump in and get right to the topic of the day. But we're going to kick off this journey in a slightly different way. One that I know is going to make a huge impression on you as well as set one of the most important core principles of this book.

I want to paint a picture for you that I'm going to ask you to step into with me. One that is going to create an experience for you in ways that might surprise you. So, take a deep breath, focus on this moment, and go with me on this.

Ready? Let's get started.

Imagine that you're in the middle of the Sahara Desert. Today the temperature is a stifling 122 degrees. You've been walking for hours, and you're completely covered in sweat. But you're getting close to the where you're too hot to sweat. In fact, you're feeling like you don't have a drop of water left in your body anymore.

There's nothing above you to stop the sun beating down on your head and your skin is beginning to sear. Your lips are feeling like sandpaper and your mouth feels like cotton. The sun is beating down from above and reflecting strongly up at you from the sand.

All you want is water. And there's none to be found anywhere.

You're trudging through the desert with no sign of relief in sight. It's at that moment that you see something that breaks up the miles of rolling sand. As you get closer to whatever it is, you get a little lift of energy, enough to keep moving. When you get close enough to determine what it is, you discover that it's a tree.

It might not be an oasis, but at the very least it'll provide some shade. So, you get there as quickly as you can. And for the first time in forever, the sun isn't beating down on your head. You've found a little bit of shade. And a trickle of gratitude starts to flow through your body.

As you look up, you discover that your newfound shade is actually a lemon tree. Without hesitation, you grab a lemon and pluck it from the branch. You can already feel the sourness of the juice in your cheeks. Your mouth starts to water as you hold that lemon in your hand. You don't care about how sour or stinging it might be to taste. All you care about is that there is water on the inside.

As you peel that lemon, a burst of citrus scent somehow brings even more relief. And at that moment a slight but perceivable breeze brushes past your skin. Things are looking up, slowly but surely.

When you finish peeling the lemon, you pull off a piece and stick it in your mouth. The sourness burns your lips. The juice sears your throat as it goes down. Yet at the same time, you feel relief and gratitude. The next piece of lemon doesn't burn nearly as much. Your mouth still waters but with a lot less fervor. And the breeze picks back up again. Slowly, your energy returns. You feel a sense of gratitude for the little relief that you've received. The tree and the lemon were a godsend of their very own.

Now take a deep breath, come back to where you are at this moment, and tell me this: what happened when you read this story? Could you see yourself in the situation?

And more importantly...could you FEEL yourself in it?

Now, I don't want to make too many suggestions (as I've already created quite the scenario), but I do want you to think about this: what did you feel in your body during that experience? Did you feel sleepy, scared, hot, or tired? When I brought up the tree, did your energy start to lift a little bit? When you read about the lemon, were you able to feel that sourness in your cheeks?

You might've felt anything at any point. Fear. Anxiety. Relief. Exhaustion. Any and all of those things could've turned up in your body.

In other words, you might've felt like you were there. And that it was really happening to you in real time.

But the truth is that you're probably not in the desert right now. More than likely you're in your home, your office, or your air-conditioned library. No sand, no lemon tree, no life-threatening dehydration. I simply gave you a suggestion and your imagination took over from there. And look at the way your body responded. You read a short story and it created a physical response in your body. Maybe even an emotional one.

That is the power of your mind-body connection. If I suggest something, you follow it, and my suggestion has that kind of effect on your body ... imagine how the body responds when YOU think the thoughts you think.

Think of how your body might be responding to the thoughts that you think in your head. What has your mind been telling your body all your life? And what kind of experience has your body manifested because of what it's been told?

Maybe up until now, you've told your body that it's not good enough. You might've told it that it needs to lose weight, go faster, or be stronger. Maybe you've put it down, shamed it, or fought it without being aware of the side effects.

More than likely, your body has responded to all that it's been told. What kind of an experience could your body have if your mind spoke to it with kindness, love, and joy? How would your body change if you gave it support and appreciation every day?

The truth is that your body follows your mind. It has no other choice. Your body is forever connected to both your mind and your Spirit. But the body doesn't call the shots. Not like you might think that it does.

We are all Spirits within physical bodies. We all have minds that connect with our Spirit. Then the mind speaks to the body and the body responds. It doesn't work the other way around.

So many times, we believe that if we change our bodies, we'll change our minds. We believe that if we lose 20 pounds, our minds will start treating our bodies with more respect, affection, and love. But it isn't the body that needs to change first. It's the defeating self-talk of the mind that needs to change before the body has a chance.

However, if you trade the negative self-talk in your mind for thoughts of appreciation and love, your body will appreciate, support, and love you right back.

The power of your mind is one of the greatest awarenesses that you can have. Once you understand the power of changing your thoughts, you can use it to create just about anything you want. Your thoughts can heal and empower you or they can hurt and defeat you. The choice is yours.

Changing your thoughts isn't like snapping your fingers, though. Sometimes your mind is just a clusterf&*k. Sometimes you can't quite change your thoughts because you're energetically stuck.

But the good news is that you don't need to bust out of decades-old thought patterns in a single afternoon. Not only are baby steps to new thought patterns OK, but sometimes they're the only way to lasting change.

The best news of all is that you're a powerful spirited being in your physical body right NOW. And you are a revivalist, right? That means that you're ready to take your power back. You're ready to change the thoughts you've created. And change them for your greatest good instead of your greatest fears.

Of course, sometimes this kind of change brings up a lot of pain. But what if I told you that the medicine was in the pain?

That might seem awfully hard to believe. But what I'm saying is that the pain you experience will guide you to the answer. The pain will uncover the emotion that created it. And from there you'll find the insight that you need to release your resistance once and for all.

Let's take it a step back for a moment. If you've experienced negative thoughts that have caused you pain, but you've been spending years pushing that pain down, it's going to hurt when you bring that pain out. I'm afraid there's no way around that one.

It's a pretty daunting fear for a lot of people. In fact, so many times I hear people say that they've been pushing the pain down for so long that they're terrified of how much it would hurt to actually face it.

That's understandable. But the truth is that releasing the pain usually hurts a lot less than your fears would have you believe. More than likely, your fear around how painful it might be to let go has probably created a story all its own.

If you face your pain, there might be sadness, anger, and tears. I can pretty much promise you that the emotion that went in is going to be the emotion that comes out. If you brought in anger toward your body, it'll come out as anger. If it was betrayal going in, you might feel it all over again when you release it.

Sure, it'll be painful for a moment. But I can tell you with certainty that it won't be painful for a lifetime.

Think of it this way: how long have you carried a lifetime of pain in your body through fearful, cruel, and unloving thoughts? How long has that pain been living in your body and telling your body what to do? And how long has your body been listening and simply reflecting back what it has been hearing?

You deserve to let go of the painful thoughts that have held your body hostage. Those thoughts don't have to control your physical container anymore. It all starts with recognizing how your mind speaks to your body. And from there, shifting the conversation from anger, shame, and blame to joy, appreciation, and kindness.

Once again, don't worry if this doesn't happen overnight. It might take time, patience, and understanding. But it's vital to change that mind-body connection if you want to finally love yourself as an entire being. And I know that's what you want, or you probably wouldn't be reading this book right now.

Now, I'm not asking you to shoot for perfection. It's not about having a flawless body, a picture-perfect life or the perfect meditation practice to support perfect thoughts. I'm talking about helping you become free in your Mind, Body, and Spirit as much as you possibly can. I want you to wake up every morning feeling energized in your body, aligned in your Spirit, and peaceful in your mind. And loving your entire self, more and more every day.

And you know what? You can love a body that has cellulite on it. You can love a body that has age spots and wrinkles. You can love a body that has a disease. And maybe – just maybe – loving the body while it's harboring that disease just might start to heal that disease.

In other words, you can love you for YOU. Starting right here, right now.

Think of it this way, too. Do you insist that everyone around you have the perfect body before you decide you're going to love them? Of course not. Just like everyone, you have people in your life who are overweight. People who have bad days and get angry. People that you see for who they are and love them just the same.

You have to give yourself the same loving treatment. You are just as worthy of being loved as everybody else in this world. Don't make yourself the exception in your own life.

To start off our 22 days together, it's time to bring some big-time awareness to your mind-body connection. It's time to see where it has supported you in the past. To look at a time when it might've let you down. And to start making simple shifts that will turn your thoughts from angry and resentful to loving and kind.

Change begins with you. And we're going to begin by taking an honest look at where your head is really at.

To start with, I want you to focus on a time where your mind told your body that it wasn't enough. Think of a moment when you experienced pain because of the power of your mind-body connection. Maybe a parent or a friend told you that you were overweight, and you believed them. Maybe your mind convinced you that you had "tree trunk" legs and you've held onto the thought for years. Maybe someone told you that you had ugly feet and you refused to wear flip-flops until you were 24 years old.

I know, that last one might sound a little bit silly, right? But for years, it was a really painful one for me. You see, my dad told me that I had ugly feet when I was a young teen. And as a result, I refused to wear anything but tennis shoes and cowboy boots until I was in my early 20s. Can you believe that? It's true.

His comments caused me pain and planted the seed. I took it in and made it real. And I created an experience of shame and embarrassment around my own two feet. Shame and embarrassment to the point where I created scars around my ankles. And I'm not talking about metaphorical ones here. I mean physical scars that represented the ugliness I felt because of a thoughtless comment made a long time ago.

But I was able to eventually bring that pain up and out. And now I wear sandals and flip-flops without shame, embarrassment, or pain.

That's the kind of experience I'm talking about. We're going to first focus on a moment where the mind-body connection let you down. And then, we're going to consider another time where that same connection lifted you up and supported you with kindness and love.

I had a moment where a beautiful mind-body moment made a huge difference in my life. When I was 27, I was faced with a choice: stop drinking soda or continue to lose my bone density. At the time I'd just been diagnosed with osteopenia, the precursor to osteoporosis. I was not even 30 and had the bones of a 50-year-old woman.

I knew that my soda addiction was leaching the calcium out of my body. I knew that if I wanted to make it to 30 without breaking a hip, I needed help to kick the soda craving once and for all. And this time, my mind was on my side.

My mind told me, "Listen, we can do this. We just need a little help." Now, with my mind working for me this time, I called on Archangel Raphael to make the Mind-Body-Spirit connection complete. I asked him to take my desire for soda away. And wouldn't you know it, my body responded. From that day on, I never drank another soda.

What's the Bottom Line?

- The power of your mind is one of the greatest awarenesses that you'll ever have

- You can't change your mind by changing your body

- Your body responds to the direction of your mind

- Mind-body connection experiences can be positive or negative

- Releasing the negative mind-body messages might be painful, but always worth it

Practical Action Steps for Today...

First, take the time for five minutes body appreciation journaling. Choose what you feel the most grateful for about your body and let the gratitude flow. Make sure that you do this every day.

Now, for today's homework. There are two experiences that you'll be journaling about today. First, consider a time in your life when the mind-body connection caused you pain. Be sure that you write this one on a piece of scrap paper rather than in your journal. Whatever story comes up for you, write it down, don't hold back, and get it out. Then when you're ready, tear it up, shred it, or preferably burn it.

Then, once that's done, we're going to fill you back up. The second thing is to consider a moment where the mind-body connection resulted in a positive experience. Maybe there was a time that your body came through for you because your mind believed in it so strongly... A moment where you did something that you didn't believe you could do. Maybe you finished a marathon, made it through childbirth, or cleared addiction for good. Give yourself credit. Feel what it felt like to have your mind on your body's side. And write all that out.

Let's Write This! Questions to Ponder...

Part 1: What was the moment when you mind caused your body pain? Write it down. Get it out. And prepare to let it go. You can write it in a separate notebook OR on a loose sheet of notebook paper.

Part 2: Get rid of it. Tear the sheet out where you wrote your answers for Part 1 and rip it up. Tear it to pieces. Go to a safe place and burn it. Whatever feels right to you.

Part 3: When did your mind come through for your body? Now let's recall a time when the mind-body connection was on your side. How did your mind show your body love? How did your body respond? What did it feel like? Write these answers here or in your journal.

_____

_____

_____

_____

_____

_____

_____

_____

_____

_____

_____

_____

_____

_____

_____

_____

_____

DAY 2: YOU AND YOUR BODY: BEST FRIENDS FOREVER

Did you know that whether you are aware or not, you were born with a best friend? One that would be with you from the moment you showed up here on earth until the moment that you decide it's time to move on from this life.

We're talking about the kind of friend who is there for you every moment of every day. The kind who never leaves your side. Who loves you, supports you, and makes it possible for you to experience life on this planet.

Sounds more like a guardian angel or your own personal superhero, doesn't it?

But the truth is you have a devoted friend that you might not have even considered a friend at all before, let alone a BEST friend. And that friend, my dear, is your BODY.

You and your body are together forever in this lifetime. That's an absolute. Until the day where your Spirit no longer needs the body to make the earthly experience possible, you and your body are inseparable. You're a team, whether you like it or not.

But just like in every other area, you have a choice here. You can choose to be friends or enemies. Maybe you're just acquaintances at the moment. But it's undeniable that you're in a relationship. It's your choice just how healthy you're going to allow it to be.

Now, what difference would it make in your health, your life, your energy, and your vibration if you decided to become best friends instead of mere acquaintances or brutal enemies?

Just like we talked about earlier, your body follows the direction of your mind. And whether you haven't given your body loving directives in the past doesn't mean that you're doomed to repeat that forever. Your body is pretty amazing in that it catches up quickly when you decide to make a shift. It can go from disarray to alignment as soon as you tell it to. All you have to do is say the word.

Maybe you've been at war with your own body for so long that being best friends seems like a bit of a stretch. It might even sound impossible. That's why I'm offering another option if BFFs sounds like too much to ask today.

What if you could start with a truce? How about ending the war with your body, starting right now?

It's time to stop the war with illness, disease, and pain. It's time to stop fighting against yourself for the sake of argument. It's time to give yourself a chance to heal.

You might believe that keeping the war going on is keeping you safe. You might believe that pushing up against pain is protecting yourself from getting hurt. But the truth is that when you fight against yourself in this way, you create a lot more pain than what you started with. And when you're in a protective mode like this, that pain can't get out because it gets stuck inside. Ironic, isn't it?

What about calling a truce? Declaring a cease-fire? What might the possibilities be?

Today I'm asking you to at the very least to call a truce. End the war. And from there start seeing your body as what it truly is. Your absolute BFF.

Now, I'm going to share something that you might consider a radical notion. It might even make you mad. Then again, it might make you sigh with relief and start to see a real solution to a long-time problem. Ready?

Your body is not responsible for the choices that you make. It simply carries the manifestations of those choices. Plain and simple. It might sound harsh, but I'm not really calling you out here. All I'm saying is that when you hate your body for a choice that you made (consciously or not), all you're doing is accelerating the pain.

I'm talking about beating your body up (literally or figuratively, as the case may be). Putting it down. Ignoring it. Stuffing it. Drugging it. Your body has no say in the matter here, and it's not responsible for what you do to it. That's all on you.

That's a pretty bold statement, isn't it? I know it might be hard to hear. And for that matter, it might not have occurred to you at all. It might make you feel bad for having unknowingly caused your body so much pain and misery all these years. But right now, I want you to take a deep breath, feel into what we just talked about, and give yourself a break. You can't know what you don't know. And now that you know better, as Maya Angelou said, you can do better.

Your body is manifesting what your mind is thinking. And if you don't like what's showing up, all you must do is change what's going on in your head. It's about shifting your thoughts, your words, and your beliefs to create a new experience. For both yourself and for your body.

Remember, whatever thoughts, feelings, or emotions you're having will be reflected by your body. But your body is NOT responsible for the manifestation. It's just doing what you're telling it to do. If you direct frustration, anger, and hate at your body, remember who is really making that call. It's a lot easier to blame your body. But the truth is, the body is just along for the ride.

It's up to you whether you and your body go on a joyride or have an experience of hell on wheels. Choose wisely.

Let me tell you a little bit about my personal experience and how I came to learn this all firsthand...

I can't actually remember the exact moment of the experience. I'm not quite sure anymore what pushed me to my boiling point. But one day, I decided that enough was enough.

You see, up until my late 20's, my body was a battleground. It didn't matter if I was skinny or I was fat. It didn't matter if I was wearing cute clothes or had perfect makeup. The war was raging between me and my body with no signs of a cease-fire.

All through my young life, people would tell me things like, "You're so pretty! You just need to lose some weight." I heard that from my friends, my family, and especially from my dad.

Now, I was always looking for that outside validation. And when people fed me that one big line, it validated two points. People thought I was pretty AND they thought I was fat. One positive and one negative point perfectly validated.

Unfortunately, "you're pretty" didn't cancel out "you're fat." It didn't matter that people thought I was pretty. All I focused on was the "fat."

(And how often do we do that when it comes to anything, by the way? How many times do we get 10 gracious compliments and one bullshit insult and only remember the bullshit?)

I must've been about 25 years old at the time. It was right before I got pregnant with my youngest son. I remember standing in front of the mirror and looking intently at what I saw. At the time I was very thin. I weighed about 108 pounds at 5'6". The reason I was so thin wasn't that I was hitting the gym and eating healthy foods, either. I was actually very sick. I had a parasite in my body that was literally sucking the life out of me. So that stick-thin person that I always thought I should be showed up in a way that I hadn't quite bargained for.

I was standing in front of the mirror wearing shorts and cowboy boots (because at the time I still refused to show my "ugly" feet). All I kept thinking was "Oh, my God, my legs are so big."

Now, what does that tell you?

The story was total bullshit, of course. But it was a story that I'd kept going for a LONG time. It was another battle in the never-ending war inside of me.

What were my weapons of choice? My weapons were judgment, criticism, jealousy, and anger. Not to mention resentment and pain. I had a full arsenal, plenty to keep me in constant strife, 24/7.

One day I decided that I was done. I was so pissed off at myself and I couldn't let this continue one more day. Here I was, inside my own head, fighting with myself about myself.

I wasn't even on my own team. And if I wasn't on my own team, I would never win. This battle was going to rage on, unresolved, for the rest of my life.

Finally, I said, "F*#k it. Never again. Not ONE MORE TIME will I say a negative word about my body." Not one more time.

Don't get me wrong, though. It wasn't like all of a sudden, I made that declaration, and suddenly stopped each and every negative thought. If only it were that easy, right? But in that moment, I made my agreement. I called the truce. It was my personal TRUCE day. This war was OVER.

It was my responsibility to stop the fight, not my body's. And I chose to stop it then and there.

Even though I don't remember exactly the moment that it happened, I will never forget the reason that it happened. And the lasting impact that the moment had.

Tell me if any of these statements sound like you: "I'll be able to stop fighting my own body when I lose 10 pounds." Or, "I'll call a truce with my body when I heal my diabetes." Maybe "I'll give my body a break when I can run two miles instead of just one."

Maybe you're waiting for something to happen. Maybe you believe that your body has to do something for you *first*, before you can love it enough to stop the fight. And all I can say to this is NO. It's not going to work that way. Your body follows what you tell it to. And it's up to you to stop the war. Not your body.

You have to stop the war NOW.

Think of all the energy you're spending fighting against your container. How much energy does it take to continue fighting, belittling, ignoring and stuffing your body? Wouldn't you rather spend that energy on something a lot more loving and constructive rather than hateful and destructive?

Of course, it's possible that some of the wounds you've suffered over the years originated from other people. But eventually, you're going to have to stop blaming them. I went through this with my dad. He told me I had tree trunk legs and ugly feet. Other people tell you the story, but you don't have to believe it. You don't have to add to it. And you definitely don't need to keep it going.

At some point, you need to take your power back. You have to forgive that person for their thoughtlessness and forgive yourself for keeping the story alive for so long. From there, it's time to make amends with your body and finally get on the same side. Tell yourself something like, "OK, body, it's you and me now, from this day forward. And not one more time will I speak negatively about you again."

Now, does that mean that you have to love absolutely everything about your body? Of course not. We all have things that we'd like to change, tweak, or overlook. Myself included. I do have a little bit of cellulite on my butt. I'd love it if my butt looked a little bit perkier in jeans. But here's the difference: those things don't DEFINE me. Those things don't make me any less comfortable or confident in my body. If anything, they're kind of an amusement. But no more than that.

How about you? Are you willing to give up the fight and allow yourself to find a new best friend?

Again, I'm not saying that you have to love everything about your body. But if you stop battling with it, drop your weapons, and bring awareness to your mindset, you can start adjusting how you think. That's when your body will respond.

Now, as of this writing, I'm 46 years old. Believe it or not, it was only a year or so ago that I started working out on a regular basis. The first time I've ever worked out consistently in my entire life. And my body has responded in kind. I'm stronger than I've ever been. I feel freer and more powerful in my body than I ever have. And, at an age where most of us start to blame "getting older" for not taking better care of ourselves (a BS story if ever there was one).

It doesn't matter how old you are. Or how long the war has been going on. It doesn't matter what other people think about your body. Your body needs YOU to love it. It needs you to care for it. It needs you to bring the energy back. The good news is that the energy you need is already there. All you have to do is channel it into yourself.

You may not know it, but you've done it before. Those moments when you were dead tired and didn't think you could get out of bed in the morning. But you did anyway. There have been moments when you didn't think you could take another step, yet you managed to get through the day. You've made things happen even during times of open warfare with your body. Imagine what you could do if you stopped the fighting?

How would it be if you treated your body as your best friend? Imagine if you listened to your body, talked to your body, and supported it. If you showed it kindness, gifts, and pleasure.

Before you know it, your outside will finally match your inside. Now, wouldn't that be worth stopping a war for?

Now, this isn't your usual body-image talk. This idea about your body being your BFF might seem simple to you, but then again it might sound like WAY too much to ask. Most diet and fitness gurus might tell you something like, "Just quit eating sugar, dairy, and meat and you'll be fine."

But if that was the case, everybody would do it. And nobody would be at war with their bodies. Problem solved, right?

But we all know that's not what really happens. Bringing the energetic piece into the mix is what makes all the difference. It's not just about the sugar in your diet. It's about the sweetness of your life. It's about your happiness, your alignment, and your integration as a complete being. Mind, Body, AND Spirit. It's about being consistent in keeping all three of the essential parts aligned. It's about your friendship with yourself.

Ultimately, keeping all of these things aligned raises your vibration. And in the end, energy and vibration are what it's all about.

Now, you might feel overwhelmed by everything we've talked about. I know it's a lot to take in. But one thing I want to remind you is to be patient with yourself. Be kind to yourself. And from there, just do it. Show up for yourself. Call a truce and start showing up for yourself, one day and one step at a time. You don't have to do it all overnight. But you CAN do it.

And you know what? There's nothing sweeter than being happy in your own skin. Nothing better than being your own best friend. It all starts by waving the white flag and stopping the war. TODAY.

What's the Bottom Line?

- Your body is your best friend

- It has always been there for you

- It's time to return the friendship

- What if you stopped the war against your body?

- What could be possible for you and your body?

Practical Action Steps for Today...

First complete your five minutes of body appreciation journaling (remember that's an everyday thing!). Then, I'm going to ask you to return to the journal and consider three questions.

First, ask yourself where your personal war resides. What are you battling within your body? What fights are you having with your body over and over again? Maybe it's weight, it might be illnesses, it might be fatigue or long-term health conditions. Ask yourself what battles are raging the most wildly right now.

Second, can you remember when, how, or why the fight started? How long has it been going on? Pick one particular battle that stands out the most to you. See if you can determine when it began, how it began, and why it began.

Third, are you willing to make amends and drop the struggle? Are you willing to decide to stop fighting who you really are and start *being* who you really are? Is it time to call that truce?

Once you've gone over these questions, then take five to 10 minutes and be present with your body. Be with your body in a way that you'd be with a best friend. That might mean having a conversation and letting your body respond to you. It might be repeating positive affirmations. Maybe even being a cheerleader for your body. You might incorporate forgiveness for your body and for yourself.

It doesn't matter how it comes up for you. Just as long as you take five to 10 minutes to commune with your best friend.

So, remember your appreciation journaling in the morning. Then the homework for today. It's your first step to starting (or continuing) that beautiful friendship between yourself and your body. Starting TODAY.

Let's Write This! Questions to Ponder...

Part 1: What are you battling within your body? What battle are you fighting? What is, or are, the biggest fights you've had with your body in the past?

_____

_____

_____

_____

_____

_____

_____

_____

_____

_____

Part 2: When, how, and why did it start? Focus on the most intense battle you have going on now and see if you can determine what got it all going.

_____

_____

_____

_____

_____

_____
_____
_____
_____
_____

Part 3: Are you ready to call a truce? Is it time to stop the war? Write down how that feels and what comes up for you. Then, make a commitment to yourself and your body to stop the fight TODAY. Write it as a declaration, an affirmation, or whatever feels right to you. And from there, make it stick.

_____
_____
_____
_____
_____
_____
_____
_____
_____
_____

Part 4: Take 5-10 minutes to commune with your new best friend, however that shows up for you. Be present with your body and give your best friend whatever he or she needs. Then, if you wish, write down a few of your impressions here or in your journal. How did it feel to put the weapons down and be with your own body? What came up for you?

_____
_____
_____
_____
_____
_____

DAY 3: MOVE TO THE MUSIC: MIND, BODY, AND SPIRIT JAMS

Music. I know, it doesn't sound like it has a whole lot to do with body reviving, does it? Or DOES it?

It sounds simple. Maybe even a little bit irrelevant at first. Then again, you might know exactly where I am going with this one. Maybe you've experienced the power of music for yourself and know just how it relates to your Mind, Body, and Spirit.

The truth is that music moves you. Mentally, physically, and emotionally. The words can move your thoughts and can redirect them. Music can shift your emotions and affect your vibration. And when that happens, everything can change.

Music does a lot more than make you get up and dance. It can actually change you at a vibrational level. That's a pretty powerful tool right there if you asked me!

Music is a mind-body experience in itself. I've witnessed the effects of the right song over the years, both in speaking onstage and teaching in-person classes and workshops. Every time I've integrated music into my teaching methods, the emotional and mental responses in my students and participants has been pretty amazing. When my events started featuring live music from my "in-house" musician and amazing team member, Kris, the shift in people was palpable.

Music transmutes, transforms, and shifts the shit. It changes our vibration. It can take you from a place of stinking-thinking negative to a place of appreciation, joy, and connection.

Even if only for a moment, it takes you to a whole new place just by shifting your energy. That is the power and beauty of a song.

Some music moves your mind more than it moves your body. Other music moves your heart more than it moves your mind. Some music simply makes you want to get up and dance. But no matter how the music transforms you, the point is that it DOES transform you. And transformation in all ways – Mind, Body, and Spirit – is absolutely necessary.

Because transformation like that does more than move you. If you truly allow it in, it has the power to heal you.

One way that I can catch myself falling out of presence and alignment in my Mind Body-Spirit is if I'm not listening to music. I don't mean that I listen to music every moment of every day, but I do include it in my daily routine. And if I'm not taking at least a little bit of time for my favorite songs every day, I know something is a bit off. It's a cue that it's time to turn the music back on and start filling up my soul again.

Music is one of the quickest and most effective ways to refill, recharge, and feed your heart and mind. And from there, of course, your body.

The best part of it all is that you really don't need to do anything but kick back, relax, and appreciate music! All you have to do is BE in it. Breathe it in. Open your heart and hear the messages. And if you care to, move your body with it. That's it. What could be so gratifying and so easy at the same time?

As you listen to certain songs, some things might resonate with you more than others. You might respond one way to a song and your sister, best friend, or mother might hear it in a completely different way. Music helps you to experience what you need to experience in any given moment.

It's a guide that can move you deeper into yourself. It might help you look at parts of yourself that you've been avoiding. You might find that music helps you allow in the healing support that you need. Maybe a certain song simply gets you out of your head and into your body. That in itself would be worth it. And that is why today is about moving to the music. Moving your mind, your body, and your Spirit to the right song.

How does a simple song achieve so much change? Think about what sound is. It's a vibration, right? So, the vibration of the music makes a difference in YOUR vibration. I'm sure you know what it's like when you play a few favorite songs and notice that you're feeling more peaceful, present, and joyful. Then your head kicks in once the song ends and your vibration goes back down. That's how powerful music can be. I'm challenging you today to not only experience the vibrational shifts in music but also to allow those shifts to continue well beyond the end of the song.

So, are you taking in the power of music every day? Are you immersing yourself in the music that feels good to you on a consistent basis? If not, it might be time to start turning on the radio, going through the CDs, or opening your iTunes. I invite you to do that very thing, starting today.

I once heard a quote that was something to the effect of, "Find the heartbeat of God in every sound and song." And I thought to myself, "OK, I can do that!" And from there my love of music went to the next level. Now I listen to music nearly every day. And we're talking all kinds of music. A different song for every mood, need, or moment. I've found an appreciation for nearly every genre of music (although I admit I'm not wild about a lot of metal or rap, but that's just me!).

But I've explored music. I've experienced nearly every kind. And I'm happy to say that I've found the "heartbeat of God" in everything from a bird singing and a wave crashing to the potent metal or rap song that might be a little bit strong for my taste. It doesn't matter.

Whether or not any kind of music suits you personally, you can't deny that it moves you. That's the point right there. Music moves you. And today we're going to move.

What's the Bottom Line?

- Music has a vibration and it can change your vibration

- Music is a complete Mind-Body-Spirit experience

- It can move you in all three ways: Mind, Body and Spirit

- Including music in your life consistently can help you realign and heal yourself

- It is a quick and easy way to bring joy, healing, and fun into your life

Practical Action Steps for Today...

Today the focus is how music moves you. I'm going to invite you to have an experience courtesy of my teammate and Soul Musician, the lovely Kris Voelker. I'm sharing some of her most powerful songs with you in your homework today, and I can't wait for you to experience it for yourself.

Grab your journal, listen to the songs, and allow yourself to feel into it. Allow your Mind, Body, and Spirit to move to the music...and see where it takes all three.

We'll explore one song at a time. While the song is playing, let yourself be completely present with it. Once it's finished, write down what came up for you. What resonated? What didn't so much? Give yourself a chance to experience it ALL.

Once you've experienced my favorites, I encourage you to find your own favorites! What are three of your most empowering, inspirational, and moving songs? I mean three songs that make you move your body, move your heart, and that you move your mind too. Come up with at least three. But don't stop there if you feel inspired! If the music moves you, make a playlist!

Not much of a music fan right now? Let me offer a few suggestions to get you going...

"F***ing Perfect" by P!nk
"Try" by Colbie Caillat
"The Beauty In Ugly" by Jason Mraz
"Beautiful" by Christina Aguilera
"All About That Bass" by Meghan Trainor

These are just a few suggestions of songs that send positive messages to the Mind, Body, and Spirit. And they're just a jumping-off point, so feel free to use them or not. And find your own personal favorites!

Finally, once you've picked your songs or made your playlist, take your BFF (that is, your body) out to dance. It doesn't have to be to a club. It can be in your living room, your kitchen, or your own backyard. Take your BFF out. Let it move. Show your BFF how it's done. Let you and your mind direct that BFF into loving kindness.

Yes, you might experience some emotion that might surprise you. It might bring up some unexpected shit for you. This is a GOOD thing. It means that you're ready to let it go. And replace it with something – a LOT more joy and appreciation.

Let's Write This! Questions to Ponder...

Part 1: Listen to the music. You can find Kris' songs right here: https://krisvoelker.com/body-revival/. Take a moment, allow yourself to experience the moment, and be completely present as you listen.

Then write down what came up for you. What did you experience? What resonated with you? What didn't? Jot down everything that came up for you.

_____
_____
_____
_____
_____
_____
_____
_____
_____
_____
_____
_____
_____
_____

Part 2: You're the D.J. now! Now's your chance to choose the songs for yourself! Choose at least three songs that move you in Mind, Body, and Spirit. If you desire, expand it into a playlist. Feel free to borrow some of my suggestions above or create a list that is ALL your own.

Choose at least three. And I'll leave you some extra space for a playlist if you're feeling it!

My Top Three Hits Songs:

1)

2)

3)

My Mind-Body-Spirit Jams Playlist (Optional But Encouraged!)

1)

2)

3)

4)

5)

6)

7)

8)

9)

10)

DAY 4: MAINTAINING YOUR OWN ENERGY

On Day 2, I hit you with a pretty radical notion. I told you that your body is not responsible for your unhappiness. That you, in fact, have the say in how your body manifests simply by the power of your thoughts. That's a lot of responsibility if you think about it, isn't it?

Well, what if I hit you with another idea that takes it all one step further? What if I told you that your responsibility extends to your energetic space, too?

You can change your body by taking responsibility for your thoughts. And you can change your life by taking sole responsibility for your energy. That's what we're going to talk about today. Today is all about maintaining your own energy.

This is a practice I've taught with a lot of consistency throughout my entire life. It's probably one of the most significant discoveries I've ever made for myself, and it has made tremendous differences in the lives of my clients and students as well. Believe it or not, it's something I've known about since the age of 13. And it took me 15 years to finally take it seriously.

But when I finally got it, I GOT it. And my life has never been the same since.

When I fully understood how to maintain my own energy, my weight changed. When I realized that everything going on "out there" in the world only got into my energetic space if I allowed it, my attitude changed. When I began to allow people to be who they were without trying to spend my own energy fixing them, my responsibility to others changed.

It basically changed my entire life. And I'm going to share with you how this simple but empowering technique can change your life, too.

Have you ever considered yourself a control freak? Do you feel as though you need to fix everything, for everyone, every time? Are you the "buffer" in your family or in your circle of friends?

Maybe you're the person who tries to take responsibility for saving everyone you meet. You might feel like a bit of a martyr sometimes. Maybe you put yourself last on your priority list (if you put yourself on the list at all).

Sometimes all of these things people tend to wear as a badge of honor, too. The savior. The selfless one. The one who puts everyone else first. Who fixed this or smoothed over that.

How about those moments where your phone rings, you see the name on the Caller ID, and you feel a punch in your gut? As in, "I can't talk to him right now. I don't have the energy." Or maybe it's "Oh, no, I have to answer that now. God knows what's wrong with her now." Maybe you run into certain people and you feel a tightness in your chest or you suddenly feel deflated.
Maybe you even pull back, disconnect, and take yourself out of the moment entirely when certain people show up.

Do you feel like you're responsible for everyone's everything? That if you don't step in and fix their lives, they won't be able to do it themselves?

Let me ask you something else. How well does that work for you?

We're talking about energy. Your energetic field, that is, and how it responds when other people cross your path.

Let's say you run into a certain someone and they're feeling stressed out, angry, or agitated. Maybe it's a person in your life who you've always known to be a little bit dramatic or needy. How do you respond in the moment to someone else's "stuff"?

You have two options. You can either OBSERVE their energy. You can simply notice that someone is feeling how they feel and being who they are. Or you can ABSORB their energy. And it goes into that beautiful body of yours. If that happens, you take ownership of it. And now it's yours, too. Their problem becomes your problem because you CHOSE to take that on.

When you observe, you're a witness to other people's life choices. This doesn't mean that you don't care. It doesn't mean that you don't feel any emotion around what you're seeing. It only means that you don't take on their situation as your responsibility to fix or to change. When you're the observer, you're a witness to someone else's life.

But when you absorb, you take on their problems as your own. You attempt to change fix their issues and consider it your job to do so. And as you take in more of their angst, you lose more of yourself in the process.

Now you might not have consciously chosen to do this. Just like you might not have intended to direct angry thoughts at your body and manifest pain within your BFF. But the results are the same.

I started becoming aware of this at an early age. I could be feeling great, having a beautiful and energetic day and then walk into a room and suddenly feel like I'd just been zapped. I could get on a call with somebody and feel as though they were sucking my will to live. What I began to see was that all this time I'd been holding the energy of other people's experiences. And even more so, I thought it was up to me to fix them.

Then something else occurred to me. What right did I have to step in and fix what was going on in someone else's life? How did I know what they needed or what the purpose of their experience was? Now if someone asked for guidance and support, that I could definitely provide. But if I made the choice to embody your pain and become a martyr, I'm overstepping my boundaries and getting lost in my own ego. And that doesn't benefit anybody, in the end.

See if this situation sounds familiar. Let's say you have a friend. We'll call her Sally. Sally is going through a really rough spot in her life. She's in the middle of a divorce. She's fighting cancer. Serious double-whammy. She comes to you and tells you everything that has been going on in her life. It makes your heart feel heavy and your stomach sick. You can feel the density of her pain in your own body.

You woke up that morning feeling really good. But after the conversation, you're feeling deflated. And you can't get yourself back up again.

So, then a couple of days later she calls you again. The story hasn't changed. The pain is pouring out of her body and there's no end in sight. Just like a sponge, you absorb it all over again. And before you know it, you're feeling like a helium balloon three days after a birthday party. Again.

This time you make a few suggestions, though. You recommend a counselor. Maybe a special supplement that you've heard is helpful for boosting energy in chemotherapy patients. She seems grateful that you shared this and tells you she'll look into it. That makes you feel better, too. Maybe if she starts to feel better, you'll be able to shake the pain yourself.

But then a few days later she calls you again. Same old story. No improvement, no shifts. You ask if she followed up on any of your suggestions and she tells you "no." But she also tells you that she feels better when she talks to you.

And in your head, you're like, "Yeah, YOU feel better. But I feel like shit every time we talk."

Now, is it possible that you're taking on her problem to fix? Are you absorbing rather than observing here?

So, let's say that after you talk to Sally, you call up your friend Shelly. You ask her if she knows what's going on with Sally. From there you find yourself pouring out Sally's sad story in all of its detail. And when you're done, you say, "I feel so much better after I talk to you, Shelly!"

Only Shelly's feeling pretty much like you did at first. Shelly is now feeling miserable for Sally. And so, Shelly goes to Cathy and regales her with the whole story. Then Shelly feels better but Cathy's now down in the dumps.

Then the cycle starts again. Sally calls you. You call Shelly. Shelly calls Cathy. Every step of the way the energy is being absorbed by each person on the pathway.

The original issue was Sally's challenge. Then you take on her energy and take responsibility for it. When you try to fix her, and it doesn't work, you wind up feeling lousy. Then you call two friends, unload on them, and they each take on the problem themselves.

Then they call two friends and dump on them. Their two friends suck up the negativity like a sponge. And on and on it goes.

It's not like you don't love Sally. Of course, you want to support her. But what if you chose to observe her situation, feel for her, but NOT take responsibility for her? What if when you shared the story with others, you shared it as a compassionate observer rather than a bogged-down absorber?

Supporting others and sharing their stories with compassion comes from a love-based place of empowerment. Absorbing other people's pain and trying to fix it comes from a fear-based place of weakness. That's a big difference.

You can help someone face their problems without becoming PART of the problem. That's the biggest difference between observing and absorbing.

Your responsibility is to honor your own Mind-Body-Spirit to the best of your ability. This is the only way to provide the greatest support not only to yourself but also to those around you. In the end, it's not about fixing anyone's problems. It's not about the outcome. It's about your being there, loving them as they are, and NOT making their challenges into your personal projects.

That's what I mean by MAINTAINING your energy. Maintaining your energy for the health and well-being of yourself and of everyone around you. It's not exactly the same as being emotionally detached. I'm not saying that you don't care about other people. It's more about supporting others without being responsible for their outcomes. When you're detached from the outcome, you can love unconditionally.

When you're attached to an outcome, you become enmeshed and embedded in a situation. You're bogged down in the stress and anxiety of what might happen if things go wrong. When you go down that road, you might even wind up resenting the people you're trying to fix. What if they don't do their part to get themselves out of their troubles? What if you feel like you're doing all the work?

That doesn't feel good. It doesn't feel empowering. Worst of all, it depletes your energy. And when that happens, nobody wins.

But when you maintain your own energy, you not only take care of yourself but also you empower yourself to help others. You enable yourself to love unconditionally by letting go of the need to fix everything. Or believing you have to. Because that comes from the ego. Unconditional love comes from the heart.

So how exactly do you set those boundaries? How do you maintain your own energetic space regardless of what might be going on around you? The biggest thing is to observe, not absorb. Be a witness to what's happening around you. Allow the experiences of life to move to you and through you.

It's about letting them pass through you without taking them in or making them your own. It's about remembering that you are not responsible for anyone else's choices. Observing, not absorbing.

Easier said than done, though, right? Especially for those of us who struggle with control. Take it from a recovering control freak like me. My husband always used to call me the "cruise director," and not just when we were on vacation. Always being in charge, running the show, and taking responsibility for everyone else's good time.

Nowadays, not much of anything is planned. Talk about a big-time 180-degree turn, right? But honestly, it's been one of the most freeing things I've ever done. Not that it's been easy to go from control freak to go-with-the-flow. But it's so necessary to give your body that freedom. You don't need to carry everyone else's shit in your body. You don't need to take in all the grief of every news report you watch or every violent movie you see into your personal container.

Don't do that to your BFF. Transmute it and release it instead.

So, what do you do when you observe that you've absorbed, so to speak? First, it's your job to release the energy that you've taken on. Then you need to bring your own energy back into your container. And there are a lot of ways to do this, too. I'll share a few of my favorite ways with you right now, and I invite you to see how they work for you.

First of all, I call in Archangel Michael every morning. I ask him to surround me and help me stay in my own energetic space. I ask for help in being the observer of everything – the positive and the negative – and focus on my own Spirit. And I always ask this for the highest good of myself and others.

You can visualize the color blue. Maybe a clear glass wall around you. Some people prefer to visualize themselves covered in Rainbow light. Visualize it however it feels right to you. Just be sure to be intentional. Hold the intention to maintain your own energy and not interfere with the energy of others (consciously or not).

When you ask to maintain your energy, do it from a place of love rather than a place of fear. Remember that you're not asking for protection from others. Many of us learn that Archangel Michael is the angel of protection. I prefer to think of him as the angel of maintenance. Sure, there is a lot of negativity in the world. But it's about maintaining your space out of love rather than protecting your space out of fear. See the difference there?

Be proactive so that you don't have to be reactive. Call in Archangel Michael, your Spirit guides, or loved ones. You can include crystals, candles, or personal favorite prayers.

Are there days when things get heavy, even for me? Of course. You might ask, "Well, where was Michael when things got rough?" The thing is that if you need to have a certain experience, the angels can't interfere. They can support you, but they can't change your choices. That's why you need to be conscious and intentional at all times. Conscious enough to understand why things show up in your life and intentional enough to take from the experiences what you need to learn. Without interference from anyone else's experiences.

What's the Bottom Line?

- When you observe other people's energy, you are a *witness* to life experiences

- When you absorb other people's energy, you become part of the problem

- You are responsible for maintaining your energetic space

- When you observe life, you can support others from a place of empowerment

- When you absorb life, you interfere with others from a place of fear

- Consider it maintenance more than protection

Practical Action Steps for Today...

Today, take a moment in the morning to enlist some help in maintaining your energy. You can invite Archangel Michael in, visualize a blue bubble around yourself, light a candle, or whatever resonates with you. Ask for help in an intentional way and open up to receive it.

Then throughout the day, check in with yourself. Maybe every hour or two. Make a little note of how you're feeling. How is your energy feeling? What happened over the last hour or two? Make notes throughout the day, maybe on your phone or on a notepad. Start becoming aware of how you feel and what affects you the most. Start to see where you gain or lose it. Don't try too hard to change things right now, just observe.

At the end of the day, go over everything and journal about your awareness. What came up for you? Where did you find yourself taking responsibility for things that aren't yours? Have you found yourself trying to save, fix, or heal everyone?
So, check in with your energy. Make little notes. And journal about the entire experience at the end of the day.

Part 1: Get a little help from your friends. How will you ask for help in maintaining your energy today? You can call in Archangel Michael. Visualize your favorite color of support and guidance. Maybe light a candle or say a prayer. Write down how you intend to ask for help.

Remember, it can be something as simple as asking Archangel Michael to help you maintain your energetic space for the highest good of all.

_____
_____
_____
_____
_____
_____
_____
_____
_____
_____
_____

Part 2: Energy Checks Throughout the Day. You can use notes on your phone, write in a little notebook, or use this book right here. Make sure that you're checking in with yourself every hour or two and making notes about how you feel.

Write down a few of your impressions here (or all of your energy checks throughout the day, if you prefer).

_____
_____
_____
_____
_____

_____
_____
_____
_____
_____
_____
_____

Part 3: Your trends, patterns, and energetic a-has. How did your energetic space feel today? Did you find places where you had spikes or lulls of energy? What brought on the highs and the lows?

Write about your overall energetic experience today and what you learned.

_____
_____
_____
_____
_____
_____
_____
_____
_____
_____
_____

DAY 5: DO YOU "MEASURE UP"? (COMPARISON, RULERS, AND OTHER TORTUROUS THINGS)

Tell me something. Do you believe that you will ever "measure up"?

That is, do you find yourself looking for evidence of your progress or worthiness anywhere outside of yourself? Who or what do you look to make sure that you're doing well or falling flat?

Sometimes we pit ourselves against another human being knowing that there can only be one winner. Other times we give things like scales, tape measures, and rulers the power to determine whether or not we're worthy of love, happiness, and peace.

Measurement and comparison are ways that we torture ourselves, AND our beautiful BFF. Getting wound up in either one of them is a losing proposition. I want to offer you the chance to take your power back and stop playing games that you can't win. That's what we're going to talk about today.

Let's start by looking at comparison. You might've heard it said that comparison is the "thief of joy." And it couldn't be truer. Joy is about abundance. Comparison is about lack. When you're comparing yourself to someone, there must be a "winner" and a "loser." It's a zero-sum game based on the idea that one person is superior, and the other is lacking.

The worst part is that no matter what side you're on, it's a game that nobody ever really wins.

If you're comparing yourself to someone else and you feel like you're not good enough, you're discounting your own gifts. If you're comparing yourself to someone else and it makes you feel superior, you're demeaning what they bring to the world. In the end, it's a big-time lose-lose situation.

This life is a blessing. Your body, that BFF of yours, is a blessing too. Your body is the first gift you ever received. When you align it with your mind and Spirit, there's no end to the joy and love you can experience.

But if your heart and mind get sucked into a game that you can't win, you'll end up discounting one of the greatest gifts you have. Have you ever looked at other people's bodies and found yourself cringing with envy, believing you'd never measure up to them? What does that really mean?

You're telling your mind that you're not good enough. And your body can't help but agree with you. So, you bring that pain into your container. And there it stays.

Comparison keeps you stuck.

Then there's getting hung up on the numbers. The numbers that comparison devices like scales show us.

Let's talk a little bit about those comparison devices. I'm talking about the things we use to measure ourselves. Things that reduce us to numbers like scales, tape measures, and rulers. Funny how one of the devices is called a "ruler." Sometimes rulers really do "rule" our lives.

When I was younger, the scale called all the shots in my life. It was solely responsible for whether I'd have a good day or a bad day. If I got on the scale and the verdict was one pound less than it said yesterday, I'd breathe a sigh of relief. It meant I was losing weight. It meant I was succeeding. Most of all, it meant that I was good enough. It meant I was worthy of love, joy, and happiness.

Most days, though, the scale wasn't the bearer of such good news. If the scale said I was heavier than yesterday, I would force myself to look at that number. And I would make it the basis of my self-worth. That number decided my value every damn day. And this went on for years.

Sometimes I would get on the scale three to four times a day, just to see if I was worthier than I was a few hours ago. Usually with no positive evidence.

The thing is, it was never really about the scale. But man, did I give that scale a lot of power. I let it decide who I was. And it sure as hell measured my life. Because of this, I created all kinds of limitations for myself.

If the scale was down, it was a happy day. I'd be saying, "Yes, let's do this, let's do that, I'm feeling good today! I deserve it!" But most days the scale didn't budge. Sometimes it even showed a bigger number. That meant I wouldn't feel like going anywhere, doing anything, or having any fun. I would start my day in this low, negative, pissy vibration because I was just shown the proof – again – that I was failing at life.

To make it worse, I would take my frustration out on the people around me. Through nasty comments or irritable behavior, everyone around me became part of my shitty day (and most likely had no idea why).

There would be days where I would tell myself, "Don't get on the scale, Sunny. You know what that does to you." But at that point, the scale was like a drug. I was obsessed. I couldn't start my day without getting its approval.

Slowly, though, I started paying more attention to the way I was treating myself. And one day I came to a conclusion that shocked me to the core. The truth was that I was that I was an abuser. And I was my own victim. I didn't need anyone else to beat me up because I had that part covered all on my own.

Eventually, as the old saying goes, I got sick and tired of being sick and tired. So, I came up with a radical idea. What if I just threw the damn scale away once and for all?

At first, that seemed like too big of a jump for me. I asked my husband to hide it from me. He tried to hide it. But I always found it. (Being a psychic medium has its drawbacks sometimes!)
Baby steps weren't going to work here. I knew I had to throw it away, once and for all. So, I bit the bullet and threw it out.

Funny, but after I did that, I felt lost. I felt as though I'd given up the only thing that kept me on track. Only it didn't keep me on track to health and happiness. It kept me stuck in pain and unworthiness. But the relationship had been dragging on for so long that I almost felt like the scale was my friend. A cruel and abusive friend most of the time, but at least a familiar one.

It was the validation that I missed the most. But what I didn't understand at the time was that I didn't need anything outside of myself to validate me. Least of all a scale.

When you're comparing your body-BFF to anyone else, it can never win. When you continue to compare her, criticize her, and measure her against other people – or even a previous version of yourself – she ends up feeling like an abused child.

But the thing is that even though she never wins the comparison game, she still shows up for you every day. She's still going to love you, she's still going to do everything she can to keep you alive. And all in hopes that maybe you'll give her a chance today.

That's a pretty freaking amazing friend, right?

You are enough. Just as you are right now. You don't need outside validation from any source, be it another person or a tape measure. You may know this in your head. But I want you to bring "enoughness" into your body and Spirit today, too.

That's why the object of the game today is to throw those measurement devices OUT.

Yep, you read that correctly. It's time to get rid of them at least for a little while. That idea might be like a pit in your stomach, I know. And I can't force you to do it, either. But I encourage you to at least consider getting rid of that one measurement device that always lets you down and makes you feel insignificant.

What do you use to set yourself up for sabotage? What do you use to prove that you're not good enough? For a lot of us, that's the scale. Some people live and die by a tape measure. I'm talking about anything that you hold onto to prove your worth or your value. I'm asking you to take it out of the picture, at least for a little while. And see what happens.

I used to torture myself like crazy not only with the scale but also with measuring tape. When I was as young as 14 I would constantly measure my waist, thighs, calves, ankles, you name it. And record all the results in a notebook right there with my weight. I did this nearly every day. Sounds a little bit obsessive for a mere 14-year-old, doesn't it? But it happened. And I've got the sticker-laden middle-schooler's notebook to prove it.

My life was all about measurement and comparison. And both of these things ruled my life for years. I still have that middle-school notebook, and every time I see it I remember how much pain I was in back then. But I also remember how far I've come. I remember that I was able to stop the madness. And I'm here to tell you that you can, too.

You are worthy. You are good enough. Simply because you are HERE. That is what I want you to start taking to heart, starting today.

Now, sometimes people ask me if there's a positive aspect of comparison. I personally don't believe that there is. But can you shift the energy toward something more positive when you look at other people? Of course. Comparison is a fear-based lack mentality.

Then there is observation. Observation carries a neutral energy that simply notices the differences between things without judgment.

Then there is inspiration, which is based on love and joy. You can compare, you can observe, or you can be inspired by other people. Which one would you choose the most often?

Today I want you to become aware of the feelings that you have around comparison and measurement. Maybe it's the scale that rules your day. It might be the clothes that you wear to hide from the world because you don't feel good enough to be seen as yourself. Dig deep, think outside the box, and ask yourself where comparison and measurement have stolen your joy.

Then consider the people that tend to trigger you. Maybe it's someone who you believe is prettier, thinner, fitter, happier, or whatever the case may be. Then allow yourself to see them not from a place of pain but from a place of joy. See if you can let go of the energy of comparison and shift over to observation. And maybe even inspiration.

If you can give up the energy suction of comparison and measurement, you'll find that you will have so much more energy for yourself. You'll have so much energy, love, joy, and peace ... but only if you allow yourself to let go and receive it. Are you willing?

What's the Bottom Line?

- Measurement and comparison come from places of lack

- Comparison is a game that cannot be won

- It's time to let go of the measuring devices that keep you stuck

- When you free yourself from comparison and measurement, you take your power back

Practical Action Steps for Today...

Today's challenge is to release the scale. Or the tape measure. Or whatever your measurement device of choice that might be. Then release the judgment.

Both are big challenges, I realize. So that's why we're going to do some journaling first.

Ask yourself these questions: how do I compare myself to others? How do I compare myself to my past self? Allow yourself some clarity in both areas. Remember that comparison to yourself is just as judgmental as comparison to others. Maybe even more. So be VERY aware of what you find hiding here.

Then I'd like you to become aware of any judgment that comes up for you today. Say that somebody walks by and you fly into comparison or criticism. No matter whether you direct it at yourself or the other person, just become aware of it. And make a few notes in your journal about that too.

It's only through awareness that we can decide to do something different. That's what we're going to bring up today.

So, release the scale. Throw out the tape measure. Journal around the questions of the day. And become aware of when you fall into comparison, measurement, and judgment.

Let's Write This! Questions to Ponder...

Part 1: Throw out the scale. Get rid of your measurement device, no matter what it is. What do you look to for validation? What keeps you stuck in comparison and pain? Today, let it go. Then pay attention to how it feels for you. What comes up? Do you feel lost, relieved, out of control, or finally free? Write about it right here.

_____
_____
_____
_____
_____
_____
_____
_____
_____
_____
_____

Part 2: Consider how you compare. Answer the questions below and be as specific and honest as you can.

How do you compare yourself to others?

_____
_____
_____
_____
_____
_____
_____
_____
_____
_____

How do you compare yourself to your past self?

_____

_____

_____

_____

_____

_____

_____

_____

_____

_____

_____

Part 3: How did comparison and judgment show up for you today? Did you find yourself triggered by anyone in particular? Did you find yourself judging them, or judging you? Bring awareness to all those thoughts and emotions that came up today.

_____

_____

_____

_____

_____

_____

_____

_____

_____

_____

DAY 6: VIBRATIONAL EATING: BRINGING THE LOVE TO YOUR FOOD

Let's start today with a little game. Have you ever played a game called, "going to a picnic"? You know, where everyone brings something, and you have to remember what the last person brought, then add something yourself? Only this time, I'm going to tell you what I'm bringing to this "picnic." Instead of trying to remember everything I said and repeating it back to me, you're going to tell me what you think of each thing.

So, look at each thing on the list. And tell me the FIRST thing that it makes you feel. Ready? Here we go…

- Salad with tomatoes, peppers, and carrots

- Bottle of beer

- Kit Kat bar

- Cheeseburger

- Loaf of French bread

- Kale

- Tofu

- Pizza

So, tell me...what feelings came up for you? Did you say "yummy," "that's too healthy," or "that's fattening"? Maybe you said, "I love it but it's bad for me" or "I hate it, but I eat it because it's healthy."

Numerous knee-jerk responses/emotions might've come up. But I bet one thing came up for sure. I bet that your first thought about each of these items was that they were either "good" or "bad." Am I right? I wouldn't be surprised.

After all, we get those messages drilled into us all the time, don't we? Eat this. Don't eat that. This will help you get skinny. That will make you fat. This food is good. That food is bad.

What if I told you, though, that food was just food? What if the truth was that food was neither good nor bad, right or wrong? What if food was simply neutral and we had more say in how it affected our bodies than we ever dreamed possible?

Today's topic is what I like to call "vibrational eating." And it's an idea that might change the way you see food from here on out.

It took me years to come to this conclusion, but what I have come to realize is that food is just food. It's neither here nor there. What makes the difference is the emotion that we bring into what we are eating. Maybe it's joy and happiness. But more likely it's judgment, criticism, or resentment. When you cast those emotions onto our food, and then eat the food, the energy of those emotions goes into your body. What happens next? No matter what you actually ate, it will move through your body in a slower and denser way. It won't break down. And your body will hold onto it. Whether is a burger and fries or a green juice smoothie.

On the other hand, though, if you're feeling genuine happiness, gratitude, and joy when you eat, your food will flow through you with ease. It will support and nurture you the way that it needs to, no matter what it might be.

Sure, there are foods that are technically more "healthy" than others. But you decide how what you eat really affects your body in the end. It's not about the energy of the food. It's the energy with which you eat the food that makes all the difference. That's what I mean by "vibrational eating."

You might have some objections to all this. Maybe you're a strict vegan who believes that eating animals is bad. You might be gluten or lactose intolerant and believe that wheat and dairy are the root of all evil. I'm not here to tell you how your body responds to food. All I'm here to do is to share my experiences as well as the experiences of my students and clients. This is what I've learned after a long journey of ups and downs with food. Because if anyone has had ups and downs with food, it's me.

For many years, I had a totally messed-up relationship with food. First, food was my BFF. I could always go to it and it would always make me feel loved, satisfied, and worthy. That is until it made me feel sick, resentful, and frustrated. And when that happened, I usually blamed my body for the way it reacted to the food. So once again, my truest BFF my body – couldn't win.

The key is not what you eat. It's how you're feeling when you eat. It took me years to figure this out. But when I did, it was one of the most liberating discoveries of my life.

Back when I was at my heaviest, I would go to great lengths to cut calories. Sometimes I'd go as low as 800 calories a day. And I'd do it for weeks on end. I'd write down every single thing I ate, from a walnut to a dab of ketchup. I kept track of every calorie I ingested. There were strict rules about what I could and could not have. And I focused mercilessly on the "can't have" list.

At the time, I was 15 years old and worked at my dad's fast food restaurant. When I got off work at night, I would go straight to the mini-trampoline and proceed to exercise for 2 hours. Every night. I'd push myself to the point where I dripped in sweat. All this while functioning on a paltry 800 calories a day.

My only thought would be, "Yes, I'm finally gonna lose weight!"

Then I would get on the scale the next morning. Most of the time the number was the same as it was the day before. Sometimes it was even higher. What the hell was I doing wrong?

Little by little, my intuition started kicking in. It started telling me, "It's not about the food, Sunny. It's about the lack energy that you're putting into the food."

It was the guilt that I was feeling for eating one extra almond. Or the shame I felt about having a bite of ice cream. And the pain that I felt for eating just about anything that I thought was keeping me fat. It was about the emotions I was ingesting, not the food.

At the time, though, it was a fleeting idea. One that wasn't quite ready to stick. So, I went on cutting calories, judging my food, and torturing myself with relentless exercise.

A few years later when I was 22, I contracted a parasite. And that parasite ate away at my body to the point where I became very thin, sickly, and weak. What was weird was that when I ate anything, I could literally feel this parasite sucking it away from my body. It made me feel like my insides were being eaten away, and I found it completely repulsive. I couldn't stand the thought of feeding the bug inside of me, so I refused to eat at all.

Then something very curious happened. I noticed that when I could stomach anything, I felt a huge sense of appreciation for it, even if it was technically "fattening" or "unhealthy." I was so glad to feel hungry again that I cherished whatever I could make myself eat. I began to appreciate everything I ate, no matter how guilty I would've felt about eating it before. What I was most grateful for was that I could eat what I felt like eating without making myself wrong about it.

That was another clue that maybe it wasn't about the food itself.

But then I started to realize that I was finally skinny. And I had to stay that way. While I appreciated the food I was eating, I only let myself have a little bit of it. I was terrified that I was going to get fat again, so once again I restricted my food intake. And I couldn't gain weight.

The biggest irony of all was that through this all, I had no freedom. I didn't have freedom from food when I was fat. I wasn't free from it when I was thin. My thoughts, feelings, and beliefs on either side of it were detrimental and obsessive.

Then I got pregnant. As a matter of fact, I got pregnant three times. And lost three babies. Everything about my body was disappointing me at this point.

But there was another wrinkle in the story. When I was pregnant, it was about nurturing the baby. I was happy to eat so that I could support a baby. But I couldn't do that for myself. It was yet another way that the emotions around food were showing up for me. And making all the difference in how the food affected my body.

A couple of years later, I had my youngest son. It was then that I finally put all the pieces together and understood that the food was not the issue. It was always how I felt about what I was eating. That was what I truly brought into my body.

I came to see that if I ate a salad because I was trying to lose weight when what I really wanted was the nachos, I would clench up with resentment. I brought resentment into my body along with the spinach, tomatoes, and carrots. It took on the density of resentment and would stick to my hips as though it was a dozen donuts. I might as well have been eating the donuts.

Something in me knew this intuitively. But I had no proof.

Eventually, I started to notice a trend. If I ate a piece of cake believing that it would make me fat, I would prove myself right on the scale the next morning. But then I decided to put my budding theory to the test. I started telling myself that I could eat whatever I wanted. I could eat anything I wanted, and it would move through my body with ease and grace. Whatever I ate, I told myself, it would support me.

What I noticed next was that when I ate a piece of cake and sincerely enjoyed every bite, I didn't gain a pound the next day. When I didn't bring guilt, shame, or resentment into the picture, the cake didn't permanently attach to my belly.

I started to truly recognize that the energy that I put into the food was everything. What I mean by that is not only what you're choosing to eat, but also the energy that you're putting into it as you're eating it.

Now, it's not quite the same as emotional eating. I'm not talking about eating something to alleviate depression or anxiety. It's specifically about how you're feeling about what you're eating and when you're eating it. For example, you can be in a joyful state overall with no feelings of depression or anxiety and yet still feel guilty about what you're eating. Those feelings of guilt are what make the food hold on in your body. That's the biggest difference between emotional and vibrational eating right there.

Now, one thing to be aware of is this: you can't bullshit your body. You definitely can't bullshit the Universe. If you're eating something and telling the Universe that you're really happy about it, when inside you're feeling guilty about it, the Universe won't buy that. It's no different than secretly doubting your own positive affirmations.

You must truly OWN the feelings of gratitude when you're enjoying your food. This is where it becomes crucial to look at your judgments and perceptions about what is "good" or "bad" for you. And how you feel about what you perceive.

So, think about that salad. How do you feel when you eat it? Do you resent that you're having to choose a "healthy" option while all the skinny people get the luxury of burgers and fries? Does it piss you off to "have" to eat celery sticks and tofu when your skinny friends can chow down on pizza and not gain an ounce? Then that is the energy with which you're eating your food. Anger and resentment are actually what you're consuming, one bite at a time.

No wonder your body can't release the weight. Because it's the weight that you actually ate. Not the cheeseburger or the salad. The WEIGHT is the density of the energy, the emotion, and the vibration. THAT is the weight that you experience in your body.

And guess what? This whole concept is getting some attention in the scientific world. They're calling it "nutritional psychology." And what researchers have found is that people's emotions, thoughts, and feelings about their food directly affected the way that they metabolized their food.

Just like in everything else we've talked about so far, your body listens to what you say. Based on your frame of reference, your needs, and your past experience, you're going to associate with things differently. And what I'm suggesting to you is that it's that association that your body follows. What you say, think, and feel is what your body has to follow. Check out just one of the articles published around this idea of Nutritional Psychology here: http://www.consciouslifestylemag.com/nutritional-food-psychology/

So, the thoughts that you think about the food that you eat become your reality via the central nervous system – the mind-body connection – and most importantly, the vibration you bring to the table.

At the beginning of this chapter when I presented the food list, how did you react to each item? Whether something on the list made you say "yummy" or made you say, "Oh, GAWD, that's all I can eat, or I'll get fat," you're just experiencing your own perceptions. The food itself is neither here nor there. You decide whether you're going to take it into your body with joy or with resentment. You decide whether you're going to allow it to flow through your body without a struggle or with a big-ass fight.

We're talking about changing how you feel about food.

I know this is not an overnight deal. Food is a very emotionally charged subject for a lot of us, and I get that. But I promise you that it can be done. It all starts with simple awareness of the feelings. Start recognizing this and ask yourself where the judgment comes up most often for you.

If you're eating a candy bar and you're genuinely enjoying it without judgment, it's going to move through your body without sticking around. But if you're eating a salad and resenting the fact that your skinny friend "gets" to eat a cheeseburger, then you may as well eat the cheeseburger. If you're pissed off about the salad, then it won't matter if it has 400 calories and the cheeseburger and fries has 2000. That salad will get stuck in your body as though it was a cheeseburger.

Today we're going to start bringing awareness to the table. I want you to start noticing how you judge what you eat. What kinds of positive or negative feelings do you bring to your food? Are you feeling genuinely happy about carrot sticks and green smoothies, or are you wishing you could have an ice cream sundae instead? Do you see something on a menu and think "I wish I could have that, but it's bad for me"?

Be aware that I am NOT asking you to keep a food diary. I don't need to know every little thing that you ate. All I want to know is how you felt about what you ate. And what it felt like to actually eat it. Believe me, this will tell you more than any food diary or calorie counting ever could.

All we're doing today is taking an emotional inventory. I'm not asking you to drop all of your feelings or judgments around food right this second. But what I am asking is to, first of all, become aware. Then start shifting any emotional stingers from guilt, shame or anger into neutrality. Because once again, that's all food is. It's neutral. You have the power to choose how you feel about it. And how you feel about it is really what's going into your body.

What's the Bottom Line?

- Food is neither good nor bad, simply neutral

- The emotion and vibration with which you eat is what you bring into your body

- The weight in your body is the density of the energy, emotion, and vibration that you bring into your body

- Shifting your perceptions about foods being "good" or "bad" is the first step

- Shifting the feelings and emotions as you eat is the second step

Practical Action Steps for Today...

Today, simply be aware of the energy and emotion with which you eat your food. First, take note of how you feel about what you're going to eat. Then after you eat, write down how it felt while you were actually eating. Did you feel resentful, happy, or neither here nor there? Observe all the emotions around what you eat, as well as the emotions that came up while you were eating.

Then, I'd like you to look back at your past. What were you taught about food? Ask yourself if anything that you might've learned growing up could have played into any lingering guilt and shame that you have now. Were you ever told to not eat something because it was "fattening"? Did you ever get scolded for eating something "unhealthy"? I bet that a lot of insights will come up today, and I invite you to open up to them all.

Let's Write This! Questions to Ponder...

Part 1: Watching the eater. Today is about awareness. Make note of what came up for you as you ate today. How did you feel about your food choices? What emotions came up as you ate? Write them down with as much detail as you can.

_____

_____

_____

_____

_____

_____

_____

_____

_____

_____

Part 2: What were you always told about food? What attitudes were you raised with when it came to food? Were you taught to enjoy and appreciate food, or were there elements of shame and guilt around eating? Write down your insights here.

_____

_____

_____

_____

_____

_____

_____

_____

_____

_____

Part 3: How will you use this tomorrow? Keeping what you've discovered in mind, what adjustments can you make to start seeing food in a neutral way? In what ways will you allow yourself to bring loving and nurturing energy to the table from now on? Write down a few ideas, a-has, and insights here.

_____

_____

_____

_____

_____

_____

_____

_____

_____

_____

DAY 7: STRETCH:
IT'S NOT JUST FOR YOUR BODY

What comes to mind when you hear the word "stretch"? Maybe you envision yogis performing pretzel-like yoga poses or Cirque du Soleil performers defying the body's natural limits. Maybe a "stretch" to you is trying something new that you never would've thought possible before, pushing your comfort zone rather than pushing your body.

Today it's about both of those things. And more. We're going to talk about stretching your body to allow yourself more physical ease and flow. Stretching your mind by allowing yourself to expand beyond a limited perspective. And finally, about stretching your Spirit. Pushing yourself out of your comfort zone and allowing in new experiences that will revive, renew, expand your soul.

For you, that might be reading this book! And if that's the case, I congratulate you for showing up, being consistent, and staying with it every day. You're stretching yourself in every way possible, and that's something I want to encourage you to keep doing.

Today is all about stretching. And not just in your body. I want you to consider all of the areas of your life where you feel like you're still "in the box." (And trust me, being in-the-box is not at all limited to just thinking!)

Maybe you've been *doing* the same things every single day for weeks, months, or even years just because you've always done them that way. You might not have even thought much about it up until now. But the thing is that so many of us are living with rules that might've expired a long time ago. And they're still in control of our lives without our even knowing it.

What I want you to do today is to bring awareness to the rules that you might be following in your life. Be it a rule that dictates your Mind, Body, or Spirit. All we're going to do is focus on one thing today. Ask yourself where you feel like you're stuck in a box, a rut, or a routine with something. Then start considering how you can stretch yourself to a new place.

It might be a physical stretch. It might be a new mental challenge. Or it could possibly be reframing an old situation to see it in a whole new way. And take action from there.

So how do you figure out where you could use a little stretching? Let me share an example with you. About 15 years ago I did a class called "Get Out of The Box." One of my team members, Robin, was a student in that class at the time. When I put this exercise out to the class, she brought up a fear that she'd had about getting massages and pedicures. You might be thinking, "now what's to fear about that?" But in her case, she had an underlying fear of being in a vulnerable situation, letting herself be seen, and from there being judged. So, for years, it kept her from doing something that she wanted to do. Going to get a pedicure and a massage was a big-time stretch for her, and that's what she chose to do. Now she enjoys them both on a regular basis.

Remember how I told you before that I used to refuse to wear flip-flops because I was ashamed of my feet? Well, you can imagine what a stretch it was for me to ditch the cowboy boots and the tennis shoes and embrace the sandals. But I did it. It was a huge stretch for me at the time. Now I wear flip flops and sandals with pride.

It's not about choosing something that is somebody else's idea of a stretch. The only person who needs to feel a stretch here is you. One person's stretch might be another person's everyday comfort zone. I want you to focus on what might be a stretch for YOU.

Here's another example. So many of us don't go to the gym and don't try the things we'd like to try because we're worried about how we're going to look. I don't want you to let that stop you; but at the same time, I don't expect you to force yourself to go further than you can go today, either. It's about taking things just beyond where you're comfortable, listening to your body, and heeding the messages that it's sending.

Let's say that you're working on stretching yourself in a physical way, maybe in a fitness program or in a yoga class. There might be a point where you've gone as far as you can go physically. But just because you might've reached a physical limitation doesn't mean that the stretching isn't continuing on beyond your body. You're still moving energetically. You're still moving emotionally ... just because you're showing up for yourself.

Today is about stretching, not forcing. Stretching a little bit today so that you can go a little bit further tomorrow in your Mind, Body, and Spirit.

I want you to throw out some ideas. Some things that initially come to you when you think of stretching yourself in every way. And we're going to start by looking at the areas in your life where you feel you tend to be rigid. Where do you feel resistance or fear? That kind of energy might be an indicator of the places where you're stuck and might need a little bit of stretching.

Now as you're considering the places where you might feel stuck, ask yourself what's really going on behind-the-scenes. How do these things hold you back? Maybe they create a feeling of safety and security. Maybe sticking to the beliefs and rules that you've always lived by give you a sense of control. Does that sound like a possibility?

Here's the thing. The only things that you can control are your own energy and your own thoughts. Why not use both of them to reach out, expand, and open yourself up? Isn't it time to allow yourself to have the biggest and most expansive experience of life that you can, starting right now?

You don't have to do it all in one day. Just take it one step at a time. One step that lets you stretch just a little bit further than you did yesterday.

Again, we're talking about stretching the Mind, Body, AND Spirit here. You don't even have to do all three today. You're going to take some time to journal around what comes up for you. Just pick one thing that calls your attention. One thing that gives you just enough butterflies in your stomach to feel expansive, but not exhausting.

It could be anything, too. Like I said, at one point my big stretch was to wear sandals. So, forget comparison to other people. Forget about worrying that your stretch won't be as far-reaching as your neighbor's, your sister's, or the mail lady's. It's YOUR stretch. Make it count for YOU.

Let me tell you what my team and I did a while back that was a BIG stretch for me and my team. We stepped out of the office. On a Thursday. Yep, we decided to take the day off and get out into the world on what society deemed a "work day." Think of it. It's societally acceptable to go out into the world and have fun on a Saturday or a Sunday. The world "allows" you free time on the weekends. Then one day it occurred to me that I was living by someone else's rules. And whose rules are they, anyway? Who said that we have to wait until 5 o'clock or wait for the weekend?

That's one of the best parts of running your own business. It's your business. And you make the rules. It's funny how the rules that most everyone lives by still manage to trickle into the lives of even the most independent spirits, isn't it? Sometimes they still show up, though. And it's up to us to stretch our way out of them.

Take the time. Dig deep. See what it is that you can stretch. Don't pick the simplest thing, either. I know you can do better than that. Pick something that genuinely moves you. Believe me, you'll be glad that you did. Because you'll be that much further ahead of the game tomorrow.

What's the Bottom Line?

- Stretching is vital for the Mind, Body, and Spirit

- It's about noticing what is keeping you stuck in all areas

- It's about recognizing old beliefs, ideas, and rules that don't serve you anymore

- Energetic and emotional stretching is just as important as physical stretching

- Allow yourself the chance to be liberated in all three areas

Practical Action Steps for Today...

Today is about focusing on the areas in your life that could use a little bit of stretching. Where do you feel rigid in your Mind, Body, or Spirit? What areas are you not allowing yourself enough freedom, fun, or flexibility? Start with what comes to mind first, but then allow yourself to go a little bit deeper. Give yourself 5 to 10 minutes and allow things to come to the surface.

Now, choose one particular thing that calls to you and make it your focus for the day. How are you going to stretch yourself in your chosen area? What would help you get-out-of-the-box and help you expand today?

That might be going to a yoga class and stretching your body. Maybe it's trying a new activity that you've always been intrigued by but never took the time to pursue. Maybe it's something as simple as trading your tennis shoes for flip-flops (just like I did!)

Whatever you choose, don't make it too simple. Make it a true stretch. Just enough to give you a tingle of excitement and uncertainty. That's what stretching is all about.

Let's Write This! Questions to Ponder...

Part 1: Where are you stuck "in the box"? Write down all of the places in your life where you feel stuck in Mind, Body, or Spirit. Give yourself 5-10 minutes and write down everything that comes up for you.

_____

_____

_____

_____

_____

_____

_____

_____

_____

_____

Part 2: Where will you stretch today? What area calls out to you the most? This is where to put your focus today. Choose your Mind, Body, or Spirit area and decide how you will stretch yourself today. Write it down right here (or in your journal).

_____
_____
_____
_____
_____
_____
_____
_____
_____
_____
_____
_____

Part 3: How did your stretching go for today? What was the experience like? Write down everything that came up as you expanded your Mind, Body, or Spirit today. Was it exciting, uncomfortable, painful, or liberating? Maybe something else entirely? Write it all down.

_____
_____
_____
_____
_____
_____
_____
_____
_____
_____
_____

DAY 8: THE MANY MASKS WE WEAR (AND HOW TO LET THEM GO)

When I say the word "mask" how does it feel to you? What images or ideas show up for you? Maybe you envision wild and gaudy masks that might be part of a Halloween costume.

Have you ever considered, though, that masks might take on a lot more forms than physical disguises?

A mask could be something you wear or something you put on. Something that hides or disguises things about your physical form. But a mask could just as easily be an identity you assume, a title that you acquire, or a role that you play in the world. And they might show up in ways that you've never even considered.

Most of us would like to think that we're 100% authentic and genuine with the world all the time. After all, who wants to think that they're being anything but totally honest about who they are? But the thing is, we've all worn masks of one kind or another throughout our lives. I've worn lots of masks over the years. I've let most of them go at this point in my life, but that doesn't mean that I've forgotten where they came from. It doesn't mean that I never wear masks of any kind EVER. And it definitely doesn't make you wrong if you find that you're actually wearing more masks than you thought you were.

Putting on makeup could be a mask. But masks also show up in the form of labels, titles, and personas. Sometimes clinging to these masks makes you believe things about yourself, such as "because I'm a this I can't do that."

Masks can be sneaky sometimes, stepping in and hiding the parts of the true Spirit that lives within your body … and making human constructs more important than personal and spiritual truths.

Today we're going to bring awareness to the masks in your life, understand what you're making them mean, and see them for what they really are. Just like everything else, all you need is awareness. And the more awareness you bring to the places where you've been hiding, the more you'll eventually let go of the need to hide. That's the goal.

Let me share with you a poem that was written by a student of mind. As you read through this, allow yourself to feel into the words. Open up your heart and see how this one sits with you.

Me
~Anonymous

I keep my mask right with me, everywhere I go.
In case I need to wear it, so Me doesn't show.
I'm so afraid to show you me, afraid of what you'll do.
You might laugh at me, and say mean things. Or I might lose you.

I'd like to take my mask off, to let you look at me.
I want you to try and understand, and please, love what you see.
If you'll be patient and close your eyes, I'll pull it off, oh so slow.
But please understand how much it hurts, to let the real me show.

Now my mask is taken off, I feel naked, bare, oh so cold.
If you still love all you see, you're my friend, pure as gold.

I want to save my mask, and hold it in my hand.
I need to keep it handy, in case, someone doesn't understand.
Please protect me, my new friend, and thank you for loving me true.
But please let me keep my mask with me, until I love me, too.

What came up for you when you read this one? Did it make you start thinking about any particular masks that you might be wearing? Or maybe getting clearer on what those masks might actually be?

Let's go a little bit deeper into what actually constitutes a "mask."

Some masks are physical cover-ups. Maybe it's the need to have perfect hair and makeup. It might be having the right outfit or always being dressed perfectly. I'm starting with a physical example because this kind of mask was one that I struggled with for many years. Growing up, I was taught to always have your hair and makeup done before you left the house. My mother, always a stunning woman, never stepped out without looking her best.

Back then, I didn't feel good if I didn't have my makeup just right. I felt a little bit off if my outfit wasn't spot-on. I didn't feel like myself if I didn't have my hair done. Why? Because at the time, without these masks to define me, I didn't know who I was.

Over the years, I started to realize what the hair, makeup, and clothing masks were really all about. They hid everything that I felt on the inside. And I found it a lot easier to focus on what was on the outside. It also made me understand why we create masks in the first place. To protect ourselves. To prevent other people from seeing who we really are.

Now, I still like having my hair done. I enjoy wearing makeup, too. I still enjoy cute and stylish clothes. But I can also tell you that I am just as confident and comfortable with my hair being a hot mess as I am with it perfectly done. I'm just as fine with wearing makeup as not. And I love my yoga pants as much as I love my designer outfits.

These kinds of masks are fun for me. But I'm just as comfortable with them as without them. In other words, the masks don't define me anymore. They don't control me anymore. And the reason is that I am happy with the person that I am on the inside. That always comes first.

Now, there can be other kinds of external masks besides the obvious ones. Masks can be anything we use to identify ourselves to the outside world. Things like a wedding ring that tells the world that you're married, or you're not. Maybe what you wear, where you go, or what you drive tells the world that you have money, or you don't.

Masks can be in our titles or statuses. I'm a mother. I'm a psychic medium. I'm an entrepreneur. I'm an employee. I'm a doctor. I'm a lawyer. I'm the wife of so-and-so.

They can also show up in identities that we give ourselves. I struggle with my knees. I have cancer. I am rich. I am poor. I am a Republican. I am a Democrat. I am gay. I am straight. I am gluten-intolerant.

They might even show up as ideas about ourselves. I'm not good enough. I've never been good enough. I am not worthy. I don't deserve.

I'm not here to judge any masks that you might have. I'm not here to tell you that you're wrong to wear them. What I am here to help you recognize is how much control that mask might have over you. Ask yourself this: when you consider the masks that you might be holding onto, what do you feel it would be like if that mask was gone?

How many masks are you holding onto that might've served you 25 years ago, but don't anymore? Sometimes we hang onto things just because they're familiar. But I want you to bring awareness to these masks today. Do they still serve you, or are they based on identities that have expired?

Once again, it's not like masks are a bad thing. All we're doing here is recognizing them. And determining how much power they have over you.

Part of the point of recognizing the things that hide who you are is that you have the option to stop hiding behind them. When you allow yourself to take off a mask, it allows you to appreciate the skin that you're in. Just as you are. It frees you from the worry that someone is going to like you or not like you based on a premeditated perception. You are free to show up in the world as YOU ... not the doctor, the wife, the lawyer, or the victim. And people can either like you or not.

Imagine allowing yourself the luxury of showing up just as you are without concern over what others might say, think, or do. It's not about showing up with a "screw you" intention either just to see what people's reaction will be. It's simply about noticing the ideas that you've held onto about yourself, asking yourself if they're true ... and if they don't serve you any longer, simply letting them go.

Pretty liberating, right?

Today I want you to identify what your masks are. Again, no judgment. Just identify what they are, how much power they have over you, and whether or not you'd be willing to let them go for a little while.

Take some time and really identify what your personal masks are.

Maybe you wear clothes that are too big for you so that they swallow up your body. Maybe you cower in the background in a group picture. You might cover up age spots or grey hair with makeup and hair dye. Doesn't matter what it is. Just start asking yourself where you have the tendency to cover up.

And then, once you've created a list of the biggest masks you own, I'm going to ask you to peel off one of them today. Just one. Something that will move you, challenge you, and push you just enough out of your comfort zone to feel it.

Maybe your mask is that you never leave the house without makeup. Taking off that mask might mean snapping a selfie without a spot of foundation or mascara. You might be someone who dresses up every day. How about going for a T-shirt and yoga pants for a day and calling it good?

Then again, what if you're the type who has "dressing down" down to a science? Ask yourself what might be behind that. Maybe you tell yourself, "I'm a jock" or "I'm a tom boy." But what if that's just a way that you justify the belief that you consider yourself plain or not very pretty? Believe it or not, that might be a mask, too. Your challenge might be to dress up with a little bit of lipstick and mascara or wear something other than a t-shirt and shorts.

Your mask might not be physical at all. Maybe you always refer to yourself using a title or an identity. I'm a this, or I'm a that. I'm so-and-so's mom or so-and-so's wife. Your challenge today might be to simply refer to yourself as yourself.

Remember, it's not about making yourself right or wrong for any ways that you might be disguising yourself. It's only about making yourself aware of what you're doing. Ask yourself how important you're making the disguises that you find. Most of all, ask yourself whether or not those masks are worth holding onto. If they even serve you anymore. And if the real you is a lot more worthy of being seen than the identity that the mask portrays.

You deserve to love yourself for who you are. You deserve to be FREE in your own skin. Beyond all of the masks, we are all simply Spirit in these amazing bodies. All of the things that we call ourselves are not who we are. Sure, they make up a part of our earthly life. But they're by no means who we really are.

Ask yourself how much of YOU that you're willing to show today.

What's the Bottom Line?

- Masks come in many forms, not just physical

- Masks can be identities, ideas, and personas that we adapt to get through life

- They're not good or bad, but they can hold a lot of power over us

- What masks have you adopted over the course of your life?

- How much of yourself are you hiding behind the masks?

- What is one mask that you'd be willing to let go of today?

Practical Action Steps for Today...

First, take a few moments and write in your journal about masks. What masks have you been carrying around? What forms do they take? Are they physical? Maybe emotional? Do they take the form of titles, identities, or personas? How do they show up for you? Most of all, do they still serve you or not? Give yourself about five to 10 minutes and get them down on paper.

Then, choose one mask that you'd be willing to drop for the day. One that stretches your comfort zone just enough to notice.

Finally, at the end of the day, take a few minutes and write down how the "mask free" day was for you. How did it feel? Was it uncomfortable, scary, liberating? Maybe something else? What did you discover about this particular mask and its power?

Let's Write This! Questions to Ponder...

Part 1: Identifying the masks. What masks have you been using? How do they show up for you? Take about 10 minutes and write down what your masks are, how they show up for you.

_____

_____

_____

_____

_____

_____

_____

_____

Now ask yourself this: do they serve you anymore? Why or why not? Write down your answers here.

_____

_____

_____

_____

_____

_____

_____

_____

Part 2: What will you let go of today? Write down the ONE mask from the list above that you're going to put down for the day.

_____

_____

_____

_____

_____

_____

_____

_____

Part 3: What was your mask-free day like? At the end of the day, take about five to 10 minutes to journal about your experience as YOU. What was it like to be free and open? What came up for you? What did you learn about this mask and its power? Write it ALL down.

_____

_____

_____

_____

_____

_____

_____

_____

DAY 9: ONE BREATH AT A TIME

Let's start by taking a moment to give credit where credit is due. We're not quite halfway through this journey, yet I bet that you've been feeling some serious stretching and expansion. I know I've asked a lot of you since we got started, and I want to acknowledge you for showing up for yourself every day so far.

I've asked you to take off your masks. I've asked you to stretch, literally and figuratively. I've asked you to find things to appreciate about your body EVERY single day. These steps are challenges in and of themselves.

Maybe you're feeling a little bit overwhelmed at this point. I want you to know that I recognize that possibility, and I honor you wherever you are. So, what I'm going to remind you is that feeling overwhelmed can be a good sign, whether you realize it or not. When you're feeling overwhelmed, it just means that the blessings you've been asking for are have arrived.

Feeling overwhelmed only means that the experience, the knowledge, and the wisdom that you're looking for is here NOW. You just haven't been able to keep up with it yet, that's all. You haven't been able to integrate it into your life entirely, and it hasn't become the wisdom of your soul just yet.

But all the things you've been calling in and asking for are HERE. You just have to receive them. One of the best ways to do that is to become fully present in your Mind, Body, and Spirit. And then just BREATHE.

That just happens to be the topic for Day 9. Breathing. One of the most important things your body BFF does for you. And another something that all too often we tend to ignore.

Do you pay attention on a regular basis to what your lungs are doing? Do you notice when your breathing is shallow, or when you're cutting it off? It happens all the time. You're balancing your checkbook and holding your breath. Having a chat with your co-worker and holding your breath. Asking for a raise and holding your breath.

Does your breathing change with your thoughts or your circumstances? I know for sure that I tend to clench down when I'm stressed out or stuck in overthinking. Or in those moments when I'm super-focused on skills and projects that don't come naturally to me. I cut off my air supply before I know what I'm doing. I feel the tightness in my chest, and my body eventually says, "Hello, Sunny! Breathe!" Then I finally let go, inhale deeply, and let the air and the energy flow freely again. Funny how so often these are the moments when the insight and the awareness flow in, too.

I bet you can relate. Whether you're feeling stressed, surprised, or emotional or not, it's easy to lose track of the ins and outs of oxygen. But today we're going to change all that. I'm asking you to have focused attention on respiration. And see what you find.

Sure, we're all doing well enough at breathing to keep ourselves alive. But what if you decided to take full advantage of the awareness, insight, and renewal that intentional breathing can bring? And what if all that took was a few minutes of focused attention on the air that you breathe?

It isn't complicated. In fact, it's about as basic as it gets. But intentional breathing can work wonders for your Mind-Body-Spirit connection. When you get frustrated, anxious, or fearful, you can just exhale. When you take a deep and focused breath, you can release that heaviness. You can stretch yourself further. And you can allow life to flow to you and through you with a lot more ease.

Years ago, I learned a breathing technique that was created by Dr. Andrew Weil that I'm going to share with you on this breathing-centered day. Now, I'm not an expert on this technique, but I'll show you my spin on it. It's a trick that has helped me notice when I'm getting in the way of my oxygen flow (that is, holding my breath) and helps me come back to deep breathing with full intention.

I don't know what Dr. Weil's official title is for this one, but I call it "4-7-8." Might not be the professional way, but it's the "Sunny way." And there are four steps.

- First take one deep breath OUT to release the old air.

- Then take a deep breath in over four counts.

- Hold that breath for seven counts.

- Then breathe out over eight counts.

- Repeat for four rounds.

That's it! 4-7-8.

Now, here's an additional option. If you're certified in Reiki, or you're familiar with the practice, this trick might ring a bell. It's called the Hui Yin technique, and it enhances the efficiency and effectiveness of the 4-7-8 exercise. To incorporate the technique in this exercise, you just place your tongue behind the back of your teeth where your skin and teeth touch and keep it there during the entire 4-7-8 process.

So ... inhale over four counts, hold for seven counts, and exhale for eight counts. And when you breathe out over the last eight counts, make sure you can HEAR yourself breathe. I'm not talking about silent trickles of air, here. Make it count. Use your power. And exhale as though you mean it.

So once again, add in the Hui Yin technique if you like. But start with a big breath OUT first. Then breathe in for four counts, hold for seven counts, and breathe out for eight counts. Do this for four rounds. Remember to focus, keep your count, and bring all your attention to your breath.

Then take note of how you feel. For example, do you feel more relaxed and calm? Did you have a hint of a head rush, maybe? You might feel more peaceful and centered. Or more alert and focused. Perhaps less overwhelmed and more ready to receive. That's one of the biggest goals to achieve right there.

Don't worry too much about getting your counts perfect, either. You don't have to use a timer or a stopwatch to get it right. It's only about synching up with your rhythms and your tempo. Set your internal timekeeper and just count naturally.

Your challenge for today is not only to practice this technique but also to notice your regular breathing patterns throughout your day. Take a moment several times today to check in with your lungs. How many times did you catch yourself holding your breath? As the day progressed, did you find yourself clenching up a little bit less with every check-in, or is holding your breath still a little bit too well ingrained?

Remember that it just takes practice. And it always improves with consistency. Take it one day – and one breath – at a time.

One more thing for today. As you focus on your breath, focus on everything that we've talked about for the last eight days. Take this opportunity to integrate everything you've learned, allow it to settle in, and let yourself catch up. Relieve yourself of any overwhelming emotion you might be feeling and let everything sink in. You've done some fantastic work, and you've received so much experience and knowledge since we began this journey. Today is the day to let yourself accept it all. All you must do is breathe.

What's the Bottom Line?

- Feeling overwhelmed means that you're not receiving all that you've asked for

- Focusing on your breath brings you back to presence and more open to receive

- Intentional breathing refreshes and realigns the Mind, Body, and Spirit

- It also allows more insight and awareness to flow in

Practical Action Steps for Today...

Check in with your breathing throughout the day. Make sure to also make time for a few rounds of the 4-7-8 technique. And just notice what's happening. Are you holding your breath in, holding it out, or are you allowing yourself to breathe in and out fully?

Let's Write This! Questions to Ponder...

Part 1: The 4-7-8 Technique. How many times did you go through this process today? How did it feel to you? Write down your observations about how you felt before, during, and after the exercise.

_____

_____

_____

_____

_____

_____

_____

_____

_____

_____

Part 2: Checking in with check-ins. What did you discover throughout the day with breathing check-ins? Were there particular situations and circumstances where you caught yourself holding your breath? Did it become easier to find them as the day progressed?

_____

_____

_____

_____

_____

_____

_____

_____

_____

_____

_____

P.S. If today had a theme song, this is what it would be. I'd like to share a song with you, one of my favorites from my team member, Kris. It's called, appropriately enough, "*Just Breathe.*" If you're so inclined, give it a listen, focus on your breath throughout the song, and see where it takes you.

https://krisvoelker.com/wp-content/uploads/Just-Breathe.mp3

P.P.S. If you'd like to see the official version of Dr. Weil's 4-7-8 technique, check it out right here at https://www.drweil.com/videos-features/videos/breathing-exercises-4-7-8-breath/

DAY 10: NOBODY DOES THIS ALONE: ASKING FOR HELP

How does it make you feel when you think about asking for help?

Maybe it brings up feelings of incompetence or helplessness. Perhaps you might feel like help is something that you just don't need. Then again, maybe it's also something that you might not believe that you deserve.

But the truth is that nobody does anything alone. No matter who you are, at some point, allowing help into your life is essential. You need to be supported by Spirit. You also need the love and kindness of your family, friends, and fellow man.

Today I'm asking you to ask for help. First, from the Spirit world, in whatever form that feels right to you. But you're also going to be asking someone for help in the physical world. A friend. A family member. A stranger. Either of these ideas might make you a little bit nervous. But that's what this is all about. I want you to stretch, expand, and grow.

The thing is, too, no matter what you might think, help is always there for you. All you have to do is ask. And be open to receive. There are two parts to it, and you can't have one without the other. You can ask for help all day long, but if you're not open to receive it, whatever you ask for will just sit outside on your doorstep waiting to get inside.

I bet that you've prayed at some point in the past. I'm sure you've asked for guidance and support in life, one way or another. Maybe you've asked for advice, support, signs, or clarity. You might've asked God or the Universe for a beautiful and loving relationship or a healthy and robust body. Today I'm asking you not only to ask for those things but also to notice if you're open to receiving them.

So, ask for help. And be willing to receive it from Spirit and from people. You can ask your angels, your guides, or your loved ones in Spirit. You can call it the Divine, Source energy, God-Goddess, or whatever term you align with the most. I use the title "angels" because that's where my story is. But choose a term that resonates the most with you.

Now, you might ask what asking for help has to do with the reviving of your body. Well, I'm going to share a story with you about a couple of times that I asked Spirit for help that saved my life – Mind, Body, and Spirit.

Throughout most of my life, I can honestly tell you that I was pretty lousy at asking for help. Whether it was asking a real-world human or my guardian angels, admitting that I needed support never sat well with me. I felt as though I had to do it all on my own, keep calm and carry on, and figure it out for myself. Even though I knew from experience that I had this extensive support system of angels and guides, I rarely reached out.

But there was more to it than just believing that I was solely responsible for my entire life. The other thing was that most of the time, I didn't believe I was worthy or deserving of anyone's help. Neither from Spirit nor human.

In fact, it went even deeper than that. I had this notion that other people needed help worse than I did, so who was I to ask when other people had it so much harder? Which, of course, is bullshit.
But at the time, my head was stuck in another place and it was holding up everything else.

I was convinced that I'd made my bed with my bad decisions, and it was time to lie in it. After all, I was a single parent living in a shitty rat hole. All because of my errors in judgment. I believed that because of all that, I didn't deserve the time, energy, love, or support of the angels. Sure, I knew that they existed. I just didn't believe they'd be there for me.

Not that I didn't have the experience of asking for their help in the past and receiving it with full force, though ...

When I was preparing to deliver my son, I was diagnosed with preeclampsia and then eclampsia. Before I knew it, I was going in for an emergency C-section so that we'd both survive. The surgery wound up being a success, and it looked like we were both out of the woods. For a few days, at least.

But then out of the blue, I spiked a very high fever, about 106.3 degrees. I was covered in hives and infection was oozing out of my body. Having only been released a few hours earlier, just like that, I was back in the hospital. My fever was raging, I felt absolutely horrible, and I was showing no signs of improvement. It was to the point where they weren't sure whether or not I was going to survive.

Now, at the time I'd just turned 19. In my young mind, when you're sick, you go to the hospital, and they fix you. Well, there I was. In the hospital. And nobody was able to heal me. You can imagine what kind of panic it set off when the doctor came into my hospital room and told me that I was probably going to die.

It made no sense. It was 1990. People didn't die in childbirth anymore. I should be able to take some medicine, get better, and go home. But that wasn't happening.

Just then it all became too real. The doctors were pumping me full of all the stuff they were supposed to, and nothing was changing. My fever wasn't breaking. And they were telling me I wasn't going to live. What they were doing wasn't working. I had to come up with something else, and fast.

My brain was muddled, but I began to sense that I was being guided. It was at that moment, I had a visualization, an experience in which I felt and saw the presence of Archangel Raphael. It was impressed upon me to visualize the color green. I was being guided to breathe it it's healing energy as much as I possibly could. I breathed in this brilliant green energy and breathed out the gunk. I continued this consistently and intentionally with Archangel Raphael by my side the entire time.

I was also guided to call all my family, friends, and everyone I could think of – and ask for their help. Even if I couldn't speak to people directly, I could still connect with them. I could make a request for their love, light, and prayers. So, I sought out support, not only from my angels but from everyone I could possibly ask.

I asked them for their prayers. I asked everyone in my world to send me love and light, and to send me whatever felt right in their hearts. I knew we were all coming from different belief systems, religions, and ideas, but none of that mattered at the moment. I knew I needed to be open to everyone's truth and everyone's experience. I couldn't afford to be judgmental of other people's beliefs. There was no time to hesitate about asking, either. I was ready to take love and healing in whatever way that it was given to me.

So, for the next 12 hours, I asked for help. And I was open to receive it. I continued the visualization. The green in, the gunk out. I was breathing in, my arms were outstretched, and I stayed open to all the love, healing, and energy that I could receive.

Twelve hours later, my fever broke. The next day, I checked myself out of the hospital. That's how quickly things turned around. Now, I wasn't entirely healed. My parents nursed me back to health in their home for about a month or so before I felt like myself again. But the results of the experience were undeniable.

Archangel Raphael was with me. I allowed myself to receive that healing energy. And this was the first time that I ever consciously remembered it. It was a mind-blowingly amazing, life-saving experience.

But despite the power of that experience, somehow, I forgot that I had an entire host of angels ready and willing to help me. Those feelings of unworthiness started creeping back in again, and "life" started happening again.

At the age of 28, I was diagnosed with osteopenia, the precursor to osteoporosis. I wasn't even 30, yet they told me I had the bones of a 40 to a 50-year-old woman. And you don't grow any new bone after age 30. They told me that five factors predisposed you to osteoporosis, and wouldn't you know it, I had all five of them. Being thin, check. Not doing enough weight-bearing exercise, check. Not consuming dairy or taking calcium, check, check. Drinking too much soda, check.

My doctors were saying I should start on medication immediately, but I wasn't having that. What was I willing to do? As I looked at that top five predisposing factors as possible changes I could make, nothing looked appealing. Or even doable. I wasn't going to take calcium because I had no interest in swallowing horse pills. I wasn't going to drink milk because I didn't like it. There was no way I wanted to gain more weight because I liked the size that I was. And you'd never catch me at the gym, so that took care of working out. What was left?

Cutting out soda was the only option left. And at the time, I was a full-on soda addict. We're talking about someone who consumed at least a two-liter bottle of Diet Dr. Pepper every day. Clearly, the gauntlet had been thrown down.

I was sitting in my kitchen on a Thursday afternoon. All I kept thinking was that soda had to go, and for a lot of reasons. I knew it was terrible for my teeth. It didn't even make me feel good to drink it anymore. And now it was literally eating away at my bones. But despite all the evidence that I had to stop drinking it, soda had this power over me. It wasn't as though I hadn't tried several times before. Nothing ever seemed to work. The desire for the soda was nothing short of obsessive. I knew if I planned to save my own bones, I was going to need help from a higher power.

I knew I could force myself to stop drinking soda, at least for a little while. That wasn't the issue. The problem was the obsessive desire to drink it. So, I called on Archangel Raphael, and I asked him to help me release the need, the craving for the soda. So, I stood in my kitchen, and I said, "OK, Archangel Raphael, I need help. I need you to help me not WANT the soda." I asked sincerely, and with an open heart. And I let it go.

After that day, I never had the desire for soda again. Ever. The most exciting part is that I didn't push, I didn't try too hard. All I did was ask for help. And just like that, I received the support that I needed. The desire for the soda was gone, and it never returned.

These are just a couple of examples of what is possible when you reach out for spiritual support and you allow yourself to let it in. This kind of help is available to you at all times, and I want you to start experiencing it today.

So today, I want you to ask for help. Start with asking for help from the Spirit world. For you, this might be asking angels, guides, or loved ones in Spirit. It might be God, the Universe, or Source energy. Doesn't matter to me, so long as it makes sense to YOU.

You can ask for physical healing if that's what you need. Maybe emotional healing, if that's what you wish for. You might be seeking spiritual or mental healing. But the thing is, you don't even need to know what you're asking for, necessarily. Spirit has a way of knowing what you need, even if you're not absolutely sure yourself just yet. But you do have to ask. That part is up to you.

In both of the stories I shared with you, I called on Archangel Raphael. I visualized the color green. And I opened up both my arms and my heart to receive his healing energy. Feel free to use that yourself if it resonates with you.

Connecting with Spirit and requesting support is the first part of your homework. The second part is to ask an actual living, breathing person for assistance today. It could be that you ask for help with, say, fixing your computer. Maybe it's asking a stranger for directions. You call up a friend and ask them for some support or help in a situation that you've been dealing with. Maybe it's even asking for love, light, or prayers on your Facebook page. It all counts.

As you go through the process, notice how you feel before you ask and after you ask. How does it make you feel to ask for help from Spirit or angels? What does it feel like to ask another human for help? You might notice that asking one is more comfortable than the other. Maybe you hesitate in requesting help from a person more than you do an Archangel. Then again, for you it might be the other way around.

Why is it so important to reach out for assistance? Because, my friend, you deserve it. You deserve advice, support, guidance, and direction. So many of us are trained to do everything on our own. You've probably heard all the lines touting the virtues of self-sufficiency. If you want something done right, do it yourself. You don't need help. You don't deserve support.

The stories we tell ourselves are numerous. The stories we learn from the world are many. You don't have to let those stories live on any longer. You deserve love, support, health, happiness, and joy. And you don't have to do everything in this life on your own.

So, get out there, open your arms, open your heart, and say, "I am open to receive this love, this light, these healings, these prayers." Call on Archangel Raphael, God and Goddess, or the Universe. Ask a friend, a family member, a co-worker or a stranger to give you the lift that you need. Be open. Jump in. Ask for help and be open to receive.

What's the Bottom Line?

- Most of us haven't been taught to ask for help

- You might feel like you don't need it

- You might feel unworthy to receive

- Asking for help is a sign of strength, not weakness

- You must not only ask, but also be open to receive

- Ask for help from Spirit and people

Practical Action Steps for Today...

Like we talked about, today's homework has two parts. First, connect with Spirit and send out your request, whatever it may be. You could speak to Spirit, your angels, the Universe, or the God of your understanding. If you know what you need, be specific. Ask to be released from the need for this or ask for help to heal that. Do whatever feels in alignment for you.

Second, seek out the support of a fellow human being. It could be a friend, a co-worker, a family member, or an acquaintance. It might even be a stranger. Here's the challenge, too: make it something that expands you, that pushes your comfort zone just enough to notice.

It might be asking your husband to help you with the laundry. Maybe for you, it's calling a friend and asking for support and advice with a something that's been on your mind. It could even be asking a stranger to grab something for you off of the top shelf at the grocery store. It doesn't matter what it is. Just make it something that pushes your limits just enough to feel a little bit uncomfortable. (Because after all, if it's comfortable, you already know how to do it.)

After all is said and done, ask yourself this: what did it feel like to ask for help? How did you feel before and after the fact? What kind of response did you receive, both from Spirit and from the other person? Was it more comfortable to ask for help from Spirit, or from another person?

Let's Write This! Questions to Ponder...

Part 1: Asking Spirit for help. How did you choose to ask for help from Spirit? Who did you call on? What did you ask for help with?

_____
_____
_____
_____
_____
_____

What was the response? Did you receive an immediate response, or did the answer show up for you later?

_____
_____
_____
_____
_____
_____

How did it feel before you asked, as opposed to after you asked? Write down a little bit about your experience here.

_____
_____
_____
_____
_____
_____

Part 2: Asking someone for help. How did you choose to ask for help from your fellow humans? Who did you call on? What did you ask for help with?

_____

_____

_____

_____

_____

_____

_____

_____

_____

What was the response? What kind of response did you get from the other person, both physically and spiritually? Were they surprised, taken aback, pleased, or something else?

_____

_____

_____

_____

_____

_____

_____

_____

_____

How did it feel before you asked as opposed to after you asked? Were you nervous before you asked, or maybe excited? What did it feel like afterward?

_____

_____

_____

_____

_____

_____

_____

_____

_____

Part 3: What was the difference for you? Was it more natural for you to ask an angel or a person? Which one feels safer to you? Which one is more of a challenge? Where do you feel the need to expand?

_____
_____
_____
_____
_____
_____
_____
_____
_____
_____

Part 4: What stories have you held onto in the past, and which ones are you willing to drop? What stories have you always told yourself about asking for help? That you don't need it, that you don't deserve it, or maybe something else? Is there a story that you're willing to let go of now?

_____
_____
_____
_____
_____
_____
_____
_____
_____
_____

DAY 11: TIME FOR A NEW (BODY) STORY?

Stories. We all have a lot of them in our personal libraries. Yesterday we touched on stories that you might've told yourself over the years about reaching out for help, and how holding onto those stories does a lot more harm than good. I bet as we've gone through this challenge, you've uncovered a lot of old tapes about all the topics we've discussed. Things that might've been playing in your head for so long that you didn't realize they were there until you shined a light on them.

Today we're going to focus on a specific kind of story. Your BODY stories. We're going to look at your old tapes that have been on "repeat" in regard to your physical container. We're going to get to the bottom of the tale that your head has created about your BFF. And from there, we're going to create a whole new storyline that is worthy of the best friend you'll ever have.

I can tell you with complete honesty that re-writing my body story took me many years. It was a taxing and lengthy journey for me, but that doesn't mean the road has to be that long for you. Maybe you've already been on a long journey, and you're over the old story already. It might be that you've been preparing to let go of a repeating loop that has been playing for decades, and you're ready now.

That was the point that it got to for me. I was in a constant battle with my body, and I had no idea that we were supposed to be friends. It took a lot of painful experiences before I understood that my body just wanted to support me, and I was making that task nearly impossible. When my head finally caught up with my Spirit, my body was able to follow. I was able to release the pain, crush the old tapes that had been playing for decades, and finally record a new song.

If you're anything like I was, you might be harboring pain that has been causing you to view your body with anger, shame or resentment. The thing is, the longer that those thoughts are running the show, the longer your body will continue to tell that story. But here's the cool part: your body follows where your mind goes. So, if you can build a running story on self-defeating thoughts, you can also create a happy ending by shifting to thoughts of kindness, love, and joy. Ultimately, the choice is yours.

Not to say that changing your thoughts is as simple as the wave of a magic wand. You must release the pain that caused the symptom in the first place, and that can be a pretty daunting task. Still, if you've brought low-vibrational emotions into your body, they're going to stay there until they're told otherwise.

That's just it … if you want to heal, you've got to remove the cause. Not just the symptom. If you've taken pain into your body, the only way to get it out is to move it through.

Anything that you hold onto stays stuck in your body. If you bring emotions into your body and you cling to it, it feeds on itself. Your mind creates a story based on the emotions that repeat themselves. And from there, your body tells the same story over and over again.

If all this time your internal dialogue was based on pain, fear, and shame, how might the story change if you switched the foundation to kindness, gratitude, and appreciation?

Today you're going to edit the old tapes. Create a new story. And start telling it every day.

Now, you might be wondering what exactly constitutes a "body story." I've had many of them haunting me over the years, so let me share a few of my best examples:
Ever told yourself something like, "you're big-boned?" That's pretty much another way of saying "your fat." I grew up in a family where nearly all the women on my mother's side saw weight as a struggle. Even though my mom was always the perfect weight, she seemed to be in a constant battle to stay that way. So, it became my perception (and my story) that maintaining your weight was always going to be a battle.

I had plenty of evidence to support that story, too. Every time there was a family celebration, there'd be food. And where there was food, there were judgments. The constant joke in my family was that "You're a Nordall." The translation? You'd always be at odds with food. You were destined to struggle with your weight from here on out. So, you better watch what you eat at every moment.

Then there was the other story. I couldn't lose weight. I'm always going to be fat. I'm big-boned, so what would it matter if I lost weight or not? I was in a battle that I couldn't win. And the story I told about it made the struggle real.

After I had my son, I came across a book that changed the course of my life, Louise Hay's *"You Can Heal Your Life."* It was my introduction to the world of positive thinking, something that I'd only had inklings about up until that point. The core idea of Louise Hay's book was a simple one: replace your negative thoughts with positive ones, and eventually, your outer world would catch up. It seemed simple enough in theory. The practice, however, was another matter.

When I broke down and looked at the thoughts I had always had about my body, I realized that nearly every single one was demeaning. I was too fat. I was too big. My body didn't look the way I wanted it to. It never would, so what was the point in trying? (Or so the old stories would have me believe.)

Still, I thought I'd give this positive thinking thing a try. That's when I shifted my language. I got my affirmation game going and hoped for the best. I came up with lines like, "I am healthy. I am thin. I am strong. I am physically fit." I repeated these words over and over again. That was the easy part. But did I believe them? Not so much. It felt like an ironic joke that I was making up. And even worse, I didn't see any changes happening on the outside.

But according to what the book said, affirmations were more of a "fake it till you make it" kind of game. In other words, the more you repeated your positive affirmations, the more they'd sink in. Eventually, you would start to believe what you told yourself. Maybe it wouldn't happen overnight. But theoretically, with enough repetition, I should be able to convince myself that I was that fit, strong, powerful woman.

So, I carried on with my affirmations ... but at the same time, I told myself that they were bullshit. I'd say, "I am healthy." Then right away I'd counter with, "Nope, that's not true." I'd tell myself I was thin only to say right back, "No, you're not." I was saying all the right things but shooting them all down as fast as they came out of my mouth. Pretty soon, the only thing I was telling myself was that what I was doing wasn't working. My life and my body were the same, and I was feeling like a fool for lying to myself.

But then something occurred to me. Maybe my life didn't magically transform the minute I started reciting all this happy self-talk. But if I kept thinking these happy thoughts, what was the worst that could happen? Nothing would happen at all. I'd be no worse off than I already was. And what was the best that might happen? I might start feeling better ... even if only a little bit.

Maybe I was addicted to being in pain. Perhaps all that I knew was being a victim, and that role was comfortable for me. Perhaps it was high time to start breaking that cycle and start seeing myself in a whole new light. That meant thinking, doing, and being something different. It was worth a try because I sure didn't have anything to lose.

So, I kept on saying those affirmations. I got more consistent with it. And I added other tools, too. I called on the angels. I asked Archangel Michael to help me maintain my energy, I brought in every tip, trick, and technique that I knew how to use. And lo and behold, eventually, I started noticing changes in my energy. Little by little, I began to feel a little lighter, happier, and stronger. And then one day, the aha to end all "ahas" showed up.

What I realized was this: all of my positive affirmations had felt like bullshit to me for the longest time. But what if I had it backwards? What if the truth was that the NEGATIVE thoughts were the real bullshit? Maybe I only ever believed the lousy stuff because other people told me it was true. Or society insisted that it was true. Maybe I was perfectly fine the way I was born. And for whatever reason, I decided to buy into the bullshit that the world was selling me.

I finally realized that I had a choice about what I thought, what I believed, and how I felt. I knew that I had empowered the negative stories about myself for years. Why not try enabling a tale that loved me back for a change?

That's just what I did. My new story was, "I am a healthy, strong, thin, energetic woman. I attract a loving partner who loves me unconditionally, supports my journey and sees my beauty in those moments where I don't." I traded the old story for the new one. And over the next couple of years, that was the story that became by everyday reality.

Now, I'm not going to lie – even after my big aha, I still felt like I was bullshitting myself for a long time. But eventually, telling my new story became second nature. There wasn't a big magical moment where I realized, "Oh, wait, I'm there!" It was my awareness that shifted, subtly but surely. I realized one day that I didn't feel as much angst towards myself anymore. When people made snarky comments in my direction, they didn't hurt as much as they once did. I finally knew who I was. And I was living the story of my dreams.

What if all of those stinking thinking things you've ever believed about yourself just weren't true? What if you only thought them because of the stories other people told you? What if you only bought into all the lies because you saw it in society or saw it on TV? What if it was all bullshit and you had the power to change your truth, right now at this moment?

The truth is that despite your outer circumstances, you are the only one who can choose your thoughts, feelings, and emotions. You can choose the energy that you allow to enter your space. Someone or something else can't make you feel a certain way forever. How you feel is up to you. What you think is within your control. And the story that you choose to tell about it all is one that you can write for yourself.

You can choose to focus on what is right in your life. You can decide to watch different things on TV (or turn off the TV altogether). You can choose to focus on the thoughts that feel good to you and let go of the rest. Maybe it feels like you've got somebody inside of you telling you how to think, but you don't. You hold the pen, and you say how the story is written.

Your body is your most powerful oracle and your most powerful tool. It's the quickest way to determine whether or not you're aligned with your mind and your Spirit. Remember, when things like disease show up, that's just the body showing you evidence that something's not quite right. It's telling you that your thoughts, feelings, and emotions are not in alignment with the truth of who you are. It's a cue that it's time to restore that alignment. And one of the best ways to get that realignment going is to start creating a different story.

How do you change a story that you've told yourself so many times it feels like gospel? Here's an example. Maybe you came from a family of addicts, so you believe you're destined to become an addict yourself. But what if you spun the story this way instead: I come from a family of addicts, and that has taught me how important it is to honor and love myself. I understand how crucial that alignment with my Mind, Body, and Spirit is because of that experience. But that experience is NOT my identity.

Maybe it's cancer. You might believe that because your mother and sisters all had breast cancer that you'll eventually have it, too. Now, I'm not saying that genetics isn't a factor. We do have genetic predispositions to things. But what causes a genetic predisposition to flare up or not? Being out of alignment tends to be the determining trigger factor.

You may think, "Well, my mom has this, or my dad has that, so I'm eventually going to have this disease or that illness." I'm here to tell you that you don't have to give it that kind of power. Sure, you may have a genetic tendency towards something. But your emotions, your thoughts, and your feelings have a lot more influence.

Now, trusting in that might feel like a pretty big leap. But I think that you see my point here. Shifting your perception even a little bit can help you change the way you feel. Changing your feelings alters your vibration. If you can do that, you can change a story that you thought was set in stone forever.

So today I'm asking you to let go of an old body story. Just one. It could be one of your most significant struggles, or it could be something that merely rears its head once in a while. But no matter what you choose, make it something that you're ready to part ways with, starting today.

That might sound like a scary prospect. After all, if you've been holding on to a story for years on end, it might feel as though you're letting go of a familiar old friend. But remember, it's only fear of the unknown. Holding on to the familiar is always more comfortable, even if the familiar is painful. I recognize that, and I honor that. But if you want to create space for something new, the only way is to let go of something old. You don't have to banish the crutch entirely in one day. But I do ask that you take the first step today.

Maybe your story is weight loss like mine was. It could be a chronic illness or disease. Perhaps it's something that you believe will happen to you because it "runs in your family." It might feel like a tall order to start telling a positive story when you're carrying pain in your body. But remember, when you're feeling pain, your body is just sending you a message. It's telling you to STOP. Stop doing the same things, thinking the same thoughts, feeling the same emotions. It's trying to get your attention. And, sometimes, it has to sound the alarm to make things happen.

Sure, sometimes the physical symptoms need "real-world" attention. But you've also got to see what caused them in the first place if you want lasting change. That starts with addressing the emotions at the root of the issue, bringing them up and moving them out. And from there, filling that void with the energy of love instead of fear.

If you shift your thoughts, feelings, and emotions to kindness and appreciation on a regular basis, feeling more vibrant and energetic will become your new standard. It might not happen at the drop of a hat, but with dedication and consistency, your story will start to take a turn for the better. One step at a time, one shift at a time. Before you know it, you'll have created a whole new reality.

So today there are two parts. You're going to write out your old body story. The one that you're releasing. Get it out of your body and onto paper. Not pretty notebook paper … this time use paper that you don't mind burning. That's just what you're going to do with it. Write it out. Get to a safe place. And burn that story as soon as you possibly can.

Now, the story that you chose to release is going to tell you what it is that you DO want. Why? Because the opposite of what hurts you the most is the thing that you want the most. That's going to be the basis of your new story. Today's story. The story of who you are and what you're aligning with starting today.

Now, believe it or not, that old story served you well up until now. Whether it kept you protected or safe emotionally, physically, or mentally, it was there for a reason. It helped you in some way. It just doesn't serve you anymore. So today is the day to bring it up and let it go. Invite in your angels if you like and ask them to help you release the energy connected to that story.

The thing is, the old story doesn't matter anymore. It doesn't matter where you've been or what you've done in the past. What matters is that the story got you this far, and now you're someone new. With a fresh story that is ready to be told, starting today. Now, releasing the old tale might feel cathartic to you, and that's OK. That's what the burning is all about. But remember, if you're going to tell an old story, tell a new story right afterward.

Your new body story starts today. Let go of the labels. Let go of the things you've associated your body with, be it ideas, conditions, or diseases. Let go of whatever it is, whether it's being overweight, having a mental illness, or having cancer. Remember, everything is just energy. And energy cannot be created or destroyed. But it CAN change form. So, let's create a new form. Let's expand it, move it, and transmute it.

Let's translate your new vibration into a whole new story.

What's the Bottom Line?

- You can choose your thoughts, feelings, and emotions

- What you decide to think, and feel is reflected in your body

- What if you focused on kind and loving thoughts and feelings?

- You can change your body story at any time

- Your thoughts, feelings, and emotions have more power than anything else

Practical Action Steps for Today...

Grab a piece of junk paper, choose an old story about your body, and write it down. Get it out of your body and onto the page. It could be something like "I'm ready to let go of the fact everyone in my family has diabetes." Or, "Everyone has breast cancer in my family." Maybe something like, "I can't lose weight because everyone is obese in my family." It might be that you've been creating an identity around a diagnosis, and it has become a story unto itself.

Now, remember, it's not about denying a disease or a genetic factor. It's just about disempowering the label. Everything that you call yourself physically – any of those illnesses, disorders, or conditions – are only indicators that something is out of alignment with your Mind, Body, and Spirit. That's what we're focusing on today – finding those things, letting them go, and replacing them with a more loving and empowering story.

Let's Write This! Questions to Ponder...

Part 1: Release your old story. Grab a piece of scratch paper. Get ready, get set, and write out that old story. Get it all out of your body and onto the paper. Choose the story that you're ready to ditch and get it all out.

_____

_____

_____

_____

_____

_____

_____

_____

_____

_____

_____

_____

Part 2: Burn, baby, burn. Get yourself to a safe place and set that old story on fire. Release it, watch it physically transform, and let it go.

_____

_____

_____

_____

_____

_____

_____

_____

_____

_____

_____

_____

Part 3: Time for a new story! What did that old story say? It's time to put all of your energy behind the OPPOSITE of that old story. In what way do you want to feel differently about yourself? What story are you going to tell that will realign your Mind, Body, and Spirit in a way that loves and supports you?

_____
_____
_____
_____
_____
_____
_____
_____
_____
_____
_____

DAY 12: DECODING THE LANGUAGE OF YOUR BODY

Day 11 was all about writing a new body story. Editing the old tapes by changing your thoughts and allowing your body to follow. We've talked a lot about how your mind creates stories about your body, and those stories tend to create your physical reality.

Your body follows what your mind dictates to it. We've talked about that a lot over the last several days. Your mind creates a lot of tales that it sells to your body. But that doesn't mean that your body doesn't have a story of its own.

Your body is actually in constant communication with you. It has a lot to teach you if you're willing and able to hear it. Unfortunately, most of us are too busy making demands on our bodies rather than establishing open communication with them. (And let's face it, most of the time those orders we give our bodies are insistent and thankless, right?)

It's time to make the communication with your body a two-way street. Instead of pushing your body to be what you think it needs to be, you're going to let it tell you what it requires *you* to be. Today you're going to ask your BFF what you can to do support her. And be open and ready to hear what it tells you.

Today's topic is the language of your body. Knowing how your body speaks to you. And keeping the communication open and loving at all times.

If you're open enough, if you're willing to listen, your Spirit will help you recognize what your body wants you to hear. Your body will tell you what you need to release to help it heal. That is if you're willing to, stop, look, and listen.

Looking at the real issues behind what manifests in your body isn't necessarily for the faint at heart, though. The underlying causes of physical symptoms are sometimes just too deep, painful, and scary to contemplate, let alone address full-on. Let's face it: it's a lot easier to pop a pill or have the doctor sew you up than it is to acknowledge the reason that you needed medicines or procedures in the first place. It's a classic case of treating the symptom rather than seeking out the cause.

Unfortunately, the cause can't be denied forever. So many times, when you ignore what your body is telling you for long enough, it stops talking and starts yelling. And frequently your body's outcries show up in the form of chronic diseases. Or as patterns of pain or illness that never seems to resolve fully. Eventually, after years and years of the same old story, you get sick and tired of being sick and tired.

But there is a way to stop those physical manifestations before they start, and it starts with simply listening. It's about learning the ways that your body communicates, recognizing its unique language, and taking action on its cues.

Our bodies speak to us in unique and specific ways, and yet some emotions manifest more universally. But whether it's talking to you in a laser-focused and particular way, or it's sending you a general message, your body will tell you just what it needs. It'll help you identify what the real issue is behind anything from weight gain to diabetes to cancer. And what it tells you might explain a LOT more than you could ever have imagined.

One of my biggest struggles as a younger person was speaking up, sharing my truth, and standing up for myself. Sure, I'd have no problem stepping in and speaking up if I saw somebody being threatened or abused by someone else. But to step up in my defense? Couldn't do it. As extroverted and expressive as I've always been, I struggled for years to speak up on my behalf. It was as though I was eating my own words.

Funny thing, too. When I was young, I had a lot of sinus and throat issues. In fact, those problems were severe enough that I had to have my tonsils removed when I was nine. It was just after I completed second grade. Now that in itself might not seem related to a tonsillectomy, but there's more to the story.

In second grade, I had a teacher who didn't like me. To be honest, it was a mutual thing. She was not friendly to me throughout our time together, even though teachers were supposed to treat all of the children the same way. I was the odd kid out. The kid who didn't go to the church, the kid whose family was different than everybody else's. Maybe that was part of the reason why we didn't get along. Who knows for sure? But what I do know is that she made the second grade pretty freaking miserable for me.

One day, I was outside playing by myself, enjoying my own company. One of the other girls came by and asked if she could play with me. And being the direct and honest person who I was at the time, I told her no. I was happy doing my own thing, and that was that. A few days later, I was playing jacks, by myself. The same girl showed up yet again and asked if I'd let her join me. And still, I said no. But this time, she decided to take it to the teacher.

So, the teacher stepped in. She told me, "Sunny, you need to play with her." And I was quick to disagree. I replied, "I don't have to play with anyone I don't want to play with." (Knowing me at the time, I probably also added some smart-ass comment to the end, like "You can't make me" or "You're not my mom!")

At that moment I wasn't the least bit afraid to speak up and stand my ground. And let me tell you, the teacher didn't like it. And she took it to the principal.

Before I knew it, I was taking part in a meeting with my parents, the other girl, her parents, and the principal. Apparently, we all needed to get together and figure out why I didn't want to play with this girl. My mother told the principal that I could play with anyone I wanted to. Or not. The principal's response was something along the lines of, "OK, just try to work it out."

It seemed as though it was a non-event and that whatever conflict there was had been resolved. But when I got to school the next day, I was met with a shocking surprise. My teacher had made a construction paper tail with the words "tattle tail" on it. And she made me wear it around my waist. According to her, I was the one who "told." How, exactly, I'm not sure. But I was the one who got into trouble. I was deemed the "tattle tail" and was made to spend the entire day wearing this mark of a troublemaker.

That was the day that I stopped speaking up. That was the day that I stopped trusting teachers. You can't share with them. They're not safe. So just stop talking altogether. It was the moment that I lost my voice.

Before that day, I don't remember ever having a hard time saying anything. I was a typical outgoing kid who said what came to her mind. But that experience was my turning point.

That was the moment that taught me that it's not OK to speak your truth. It's not OK to speak up, say what you think, or ask for what you want. The teachers won't take care of you and the principals won't back you up. They'll just force you into doing things their way. That was just what wound up happening there.

Believe it or not, I did wind up playing with that girl on the playground. You can imagine how much fun it was for me at that point, but I decided to give in and keep the peace. It mainly was because I felt like I had to.

Not only that but I also I kept the "tattle tail" incident a secret for decades. In fact, it didn't come up again until about 25 years later when I mentioned it to my mom in passing. She was shocked and said, "you never told me that!" I guess that I didn't realize myself that I'd kept it down for so long. But that's what happens sometimes. We push the pain down. We deny it or ignore it and hope it goes away. But it doesn't go away. It stays in the body until eventually, it manifests as something. Pain, illness, or disease.

Funny thing, but shortly after that whole affair, I started having all kinds of throat issues. I got a case of strep throat so severe that I eventually had to get my tonsils out. Coincidence?
So, I got my tonsils taken out, and the physical manifestation of the situation was gone. But I still couldn't speak up for myself. And that went on for years to come.

Now, it might make you mad to hear that the teacher seemed to get away with all of this. But the truth is that she turned out to be an essential figure to me. Maybe not in the classroom, but in life. She introduced me to a part of myself that I didn't know existed. It turns out that there was a valuable lesson that I needed to learn about having a voice and expressing myself. And this teacher was the one who brought that experience to light. You see, even though it looked like it on the outside, she didn't create this situation. She didn't do anything TO me but did something FOR me. It just took me 20 years to recognize it.

But if it weren't for that second-grade teacher, I doubt I would've become the person that I am. I wouldn't be the teacher and the mentor that I grew into, and I wouldn't have been able to share my experiences to help others. And you probably wouldn't be reading this book right now.

When you stuff emotions for years on end without giving them an outlet, they don't magically disappear. They get stuck in your body; and if they stay there long enough, they manifest as pain, illness, or disease. But if you're able to understand and express these emotions, you'll not only begin to alleviate your physical symptoms but also gain a real understanding of what life lessons were behind those manifestations.

Through my second-grade ordeal, I lost my voice. What I realized after the fact was that you need to speak your truth, no matter how you express it. Give it a voice one way or another. Even if you can't speak up verbally, you can bring your truth to paper. You can journal. You can write books and stories. You can release all of your emotions from a place of truth rather than victimhood. The key, though, is releasing them instead of stuffing them back in your body.

Have you ever pushed feelings and emotions down into your body in that kind of way? I'm pretty sure we all have at some point. Maybe those misguided feelings and emotions manifested in your body the way that they did for me. But what happens then when you cut out the physical manifestation and the problem itself fails to heal? My emotions manifested in my tonsils. But taking my tonsils out didn't make a difference. My tonsils weren't the real problem. My buried feelings were the heart of the matter. That's what my body was trying to tell me at the time, and it took me nearly two decades to get the memo.

Your body is always communicating with you. The question is, are you listening? No matter what state you're in, your BFF is going to show up for you every day. It's going to do the best it can with what it has to work with. But the truth is, all it has to work with is YOU. It has your thoughts and your emotions. It has your feelings and your energy. It has your beliefs. It has the nutrition and the physical movement that you provide for it. And the quality of all that your body has to work with depends on you.

Remember, your body is just a container, and it's a manifestation of everything that you put in it. The emotions, the thoughts, the energy, and the vibration. Your body integrates them all to the best of its ability. But if it's low vibration, stagnant energy, and negative thoughts, it will show up in the body as just that – as illness. Physical disease. Mental distress. And if all of those manifestations go on for too long, they become our identity. I'm fat. I have cancer. I'm mentally ill. Then we label ourselves. And before you know it, those labels become your stories.

But what if you could hear the things that your body is saying to you and stop the symptoms before they start? How would it be to see manifestations as messages rather than using them to judge yourself? How about considering them as indicators – that somewhere, your Mind-Body-Spirit merely is out of alignment?

Messages and indicators rather than judgments and stories. Doesn't that sound like a lot better of a deal?

So what emotions are behind the physical manifestations in your body? One of the best resources out there is a book called "*The Secret Language of Your Body*" by Inna Segal. This book is the most thorough source I know of for nailing down the emotional causes of physical distress. It covers everything from kidney stones to headaches. It'll help you figure out the emotions behind the physical symptoms, how to focus your attention on them, and how to release them. And transmute that energy. You'll learn where you need to do your healing, and tips and tricks to help you get there faster.

Now, your healing might require you to do some physical work. You might need a bit of modern-day medicine to bring you back to wellness again. There's nothing wrong with that. But the good news is that you won't be taking a pill or having a procedure to gloss over the problem. You'll be using these things as an enhancement to your healing rather than the cure itself.

But it all starts with connecting back to your own body. Listening to what it tells you. And releasing the things you've been storing inside you that are no longer serving you.

Today I want you to focus on one of the body challenges you've been dealing with for a while. You can consult the book I suggested if you like, but it's not entirely necessary. All you need to do is choose a challenge, focus on it, and ask your body.

You're going to write your body a letter. And you're going to ask your BFF what you can do for her. Ask her what you need to know, what you need to release, what you need to focus on to let this go. What does your body need to forgo so that this manifestation can heal?

Write it all down in a letter to your body BFF. And let your body answer it. It might feel funny, it might feel a little bit odd … but trust me, giving your body, a positive voice is powerful. Most of the time, your body expresses itself through the pain. Not always, but let's be honest, usually it's an expression of pain that gets the attention first. Most of us don't pat ourselves on the shoulder on the days that we feel good. More often than not, it takes breaking down or feeling pain for us to take notice.

So today you're going to give your body a voice. You're going to ask your body what it wants you to know and what it needs you to release. You're going to ask your body what it's trying to teach you through the pain. And then you're going to let it respond to you. I know, it might sound weird. You might feel a little bit awkward when you first put pen to paper, and you might struggle with how even to begin. And as far as getting a letter back from your body? That might seem like a stretch, too. I say just give it a try. If you're willing to go with it, write that letter to your body with honesty and sincerity, and be open to receiving an answer. You just might be mind-blown at what happens next.

A couple of years ago, I hosted a body retreat class, and we did this exercise as homework. My students wrote a letter to their body, and their body wrote a letter right back. The activity turned out to be one of the most illuminating moments of the entire retreat for nearly everyone who participated. So much insight and wisdom came through for those who were ready to receive it. It was such a hit that I've included it in numerous classes, courses, and retreats ever since. Including this book.

You just need to get out of your head, get out of your ego, and be ready to listen. Be prepared to listen to what your body needs to tell you. Make yourself the BFF to your body that she has always been to you.

Your body is communicating with you all the time. It just usually communicates with pain. What if we could let it speak to us through light, love and positive energy? Give your body a voice. Let it talk to you on a regular basis. Don't wait until your body has no choice but to yell at you.

What's the Bottom Line?

- Your body is always communicating with you

- Physical manifestations usually have emotional causes

- Physical signs are simply indicators of misalignment in the Mind, Body, Spirit

- Becoming aware of the emotional roots of pain is essential

- Treating the physical symptoms alone is a temporary solution

- When you know the emotion behind the pain, you can solve the whole problem

Practical Action Steps for Today...

Today, focus on a specific physical challenge that you have. Then ask your body what it needs to put things right. Write a letter to your body. Ask your body what she needs to heal and to flourish. And then allow your body to respond.

Then take note of what messages you receive. Was there anything that was an aha, an OMG? Was writing a letter to and receiving a letter from your body easier than you thought it might be?

Then, if you have access to "*The Secret Language of Your Body,*" take some time to look into some of the symptoms of the issue you chose. What emotions are indicated in the physical challenge you chose? That is the kind of pain that you will want to focus on bringing up and out. Maybe it's old anger, resentment, hate, or sadness. It might feel scary even to address it, let alone excavate it. But here's the thing: it's already there. The longer it stays there, the more it steers your life. Wouldn't it be great to put a different kind of energy in charge?

Let's Write This! Questions to Ponder...

Part 1: What is the issue? Choose one particular body issue or challenge that calls your attention. Then grab a pen and ask your body – in writing – what do you need to know about this? Ask it what you need to do to help heal the physical symptoms. What does it need to let this all go?

Feel free to write your letter in the space below, or use your journal.

_____

_____

_____

_____

_____

_____

_____

Part 2: Let your body respond. Let go, be still, and allow your body to answer your letter. Then take dictation from it, whatever it has to tell you. What did your BFF tell you? What does it need or want from you?

Transcribe the communication from your body in the space below, or in your journal.

_____

_____

_____

_____

_____

_____

_____

Part 3: Translating the messages that you receive. When your body responded, how did it feel to you? What came up for you? Any significant revelations, surprises, or OMG moments? Write down what comes up for you right here.

_____
_____
_____
_____
_____
_____
_____

Part 4: How will you serve your body? Now that you know your body's wishes, how will you grant them? Put a few action steps down on paper that you can take today. Is your BFF asking for more movement, more sleep, or more kindness? Write down what it asked for, and how you intend to support it TODAY.

_____
_____
_____
_____
_____
_____
_____

BONUS: If you have a copy of "_The Secret Language of Your Body_," do a little research based on your physical challenge. What emotions are indicated in the issue that you chose? What treatments, shifts, or adjustments are recommended to relieve your symptoms and restore alignment?

_____
_____
_____
_____
_____
_____
_____

DAY 13: LET IT FLOW: THE POWER AND MAGIC OF WATER

"Let it flow." I could be talking about energy. It could be emotions. It could be the good times. (Although maybe you technically let those "roll.") But today I'm thinking about something a little bit more literal.

Water. We're talking about drinking it, swimming in it, and floating in it. Even urinating it and letting it emotionally squirt out of your eyes. Water is part of a big and beautiful cycle of refreshing and renewing both in nature and in weather. And as coincidence would have it, it has that same kind of effect on your body. Water is an integral part of life in that it provides nourishment, cleansing, and intuitive connection. That's pretty powerful for something that most of us take for granted, isn't it?

When you first think about it, water doesn't seem to be that big of a deal. But just like oxygen and love, it becomes a huge deal when you don't have any. And far too many of us aren't drinking nearly enough of it. Did you know that according to estimates, about 75% of the world's population is chronically dehydrated? That might not sound like a significant issue. Just drink more water, and you'll be good to go, right? But the problem is that even though most of us know in theory that we need water for optimal health, we don't always take the practice seriously. What's worse is that if left unchecked, dehydration is no joke, whether it's chronic or acute. I know both of those versions of dehydration from personal experience.

I can tell you that I've been clinically dehydrated a few times in my life. If that experience doesn't convince you of the importance of good ol' H20, nothing will. Running out of water makes you feel cloudy, unsettled and disconnected from your body. It can even cause loss of consciousness if it goes too far. Now, it might not get to such an extreme in everyday life. But the effects of not enough water can build up over time.

Any state of dehydration can affect your mood, your metabolism, and your energy level. Dehydration can make you cranky and moody. It can bring on symptoms of foggy and cloudy thinking. It's also an underlying factor in many other illnesses and diseases, from hormonal imbalances to digestive issues.

The thing is, drinking water only when you're thirsty isn't enough to prevent dehydration. Thirst itself is a signal that you're already dehydrated. You're already in lack mode. So, it's your job to stay ahead of the game and keep that thirst reflex from having to sound the alarm.

There's even another bonus to hydrating on a regular basis. With every glass that you drink, you provide your body not only with nourishment but also with appreciation. You show your body the love and nurturing that it craves before it even asks for it. That energy of gratitude works wonders for your Mind-Body-Spirit connection, too.

That seems like an awful lot of benefits from something as ordinary as a glass of water. But remember, things don't have to be complicated to be effective. Sometimes getting back to basics is just what the doctor ordered. And getting back to basics is just what we're going to do today.

These days, I drink well over the "recommended" amount of water per day. It's second nature to me now, but it was a long time coming. I told you in a previous lesson that at one point I was utterly addicted to soda to the point where it was eating away at my bones. I quit soda altogether, but I had to replace it with something. Did I go from toxic soda to nutritious water, though? Not exactly. I couldn't make myself go from one extreme to another in this case, and I needed an intermediary. So, my crutch drink became iced tea. Not exactly the nectar of the gods, but decisively less damaging that Diet Dr. Pepper, right?

As I embarked on my soda detox plan, iced tea seemed like a reasonably healthy alternative. But just like soda, iced tea quickly took on a life of its own. I drank iced tea all day, all night. I couldn't be without it. I even took a hot water maker with me everywhere so that I could brew my iced tea when I traveled. It became such an essential part of my life that I was afraid to be without it. In fact, I used to tell my team that if they ever found me without a cup of iced tea in my hand, something was seriously wrong.

One day in March of 2013, though, I woke up to a stirring message from Spirit. My body and Spirit aligned and spoke with absolute certainty, and its communication was clear as a bell. The voice of my Spirit quietly but insistently said, "No more iced tea." And I was like, "Ok, who is talking to me now, and why would they say something like that?" It seemed pretty unfair at the moment. First no more soda, now you're vetoing iced tea, too?

But I knew that this message meant business. Stop with the iced tea, it said. I'd already managed to kick the soda habit. Now my replacement drink was off the table. What were my options? I didn't like juice. Never was much of a coffee fan. Margaritas around the clock wasn't a practical option either. That decisive voice that I heard left me with only one choice. It said, "Stop with the iced tea. You need water."

Since that day, I haven't touched a single glass of iced tea.

Now, if you have a drink of choice in your life that isn't water, do you have to go the cold turkey route like that? Probably not. In my case, I bet that even now I could have an iced tea here and there and not fall back into that addictive pattern. But I know myself. I know my personality well enough to recognize that I'm a pretty extreme kind of gal. It's either this or that, and middle-ground doesn't do me much good. I don't even want to go there. That's why I dropped the iced tea entirely. You might not have that all-or-nothing kind of personality, or perhaps you do. The key is, being honest about who you are and setting yourself up for success as best as you can. And in my case, I knew I had to get rid of iced tea altogether to make it work.

I brought water back into my life as a mainstay, and I've reaped the benefits ever since. And I've found that water *is* the magical elixir that it's cracked up to be. Water flushes your system. It nourishes your cells, and it clears your energy. And its powers extend way beyond simple ingestion. You can also experience its power by immersing yourself IN water. I know that I have my most intuitive, connected insights when I'm in the ocean, the swimming pool, or the bathtub.

You see, water connects you to your emotions, whether you take in water, put yourself in it, or release it from your body. Tears rinse away the emotions you wish to let go of, whether it's joy or grief. Even urination is an integral part of the flushing and renewing process. It's all part of what I mean when I say, "Let It Flow."

So today it's about water. We're talking about drinking more water, being in water, and letting water flow through you.

Now, maybe you've known for a while that it's a good idea to drink more water. You might already drink eight to 10 cups a day, and today's challenge will be a cakewalk. Then again, it might be a struggle. You might not like the taste and you may need to force yourself to drink up. You might object because you're afraid of having perpetual bathroom breaks.

But here's the thing. The whole point of drinking water is to nourish your body and to flush out the toxins. That means that once it gets into your body and does its job, it needs to be released. Holding onto it not only keeps the toxins and old energy trapped in your body, but also puts extra pressure on your bladder. I bet you know that feeling, and it's a pretty painful one.

It's all about keeping the flow going. Energetically, emotionally, and physically. And water is a huge part of the process.

So exactly how much water should you drink every day, then? The most recent numbers that I've heard are that women should drink at least 72 ounces of water per day. If you move your body every day and work out consistently, you can add another 24 ounces to that. That comes to roughly 96 ounces of water if you're moderately active. Now, you can also bring in about 20% of that water every day through food, like fruits and vegetables, but the majority should come from your glass or your water bottle.

Now, I'm not a doctor or a dietician. I can't say that I'm 100% up on the latest and greatest medical discoveries, nor do I dispense advice as a healthcare professional. But these are some pretty simple guidelines that have worked for me, and I invite you to give them a try, too.

So, what do you do if you just don't like the taste of water? What if making yourself drink it seems like too much of a chore? I have a few tips and tricks to make it easier and more fun to work water into your day.

For starters, I like to drink from cups that make me happy. Things that make me feel good. For me, that's drinking from a cup with an uplifting message. After all, most of my favorite clothes have positive messages. I have five body tattoos with high-vibe meanings behind them. My favorite cups have love notes and happy sayings, too. There's my cup with the team logo on it. My favorite mug with the Buddha on it. And extra-special cups that family members have had designed just for me.

But whether or not you like flowery messages, treat yourself to drinking out of something that gives you an energetic lift. Maybe for you, that's drinking water out of a wine glass. Then again, you might like a big ol' gallon jug. Whatever feels pretty and inspiring to you, I say go for it. The key is doing what it takes to make you drink what you need to drink.

I not only suggest consuming more water but also connecting with water. That is, being present in water as well as taking in water. I've had some pretty mind-blowing insights during moments I've spent in the bathtub, the swimming pool, or the shower (they call them "shower thoughts" for a reason!). I've received some of the best quotes for my books. I've received the inspiration for programs and services. And insights that have lead me down inspiring pathways.

It all comes back to letting it all flow. Allowing the water to move through you and remove the things that don't serve you anymore. It's flushing out metabolic waste as well as old emotions and energy. So that comes down to drinking more water and releasing it as necessary. Releasing water through sweat, tears, and urination is essential. We're talking about letting go of what no longer serves you. In this case, we're washing it all away with water.

So today, connect with water. First, drink, drink, drink! Find a pretty glass that brings a smile to your face. Then with the recommended water intake in mind, keep track of how much water you bring into your body. Make a note of your experience, too. Did you notice that you had more energy or felt more uplifted? It might take a few days to see the full results, but like anything else, consistency brings results.

Today you're also going to take the time to be present in water. For you that might be taking a bath or going for a swim. Maybe even just a shower. But focus on appreciating water. Let it connect you to your emotions and see what comes up for you.

Lastly, remember to release water as you need to. Regular bathroom breaks are not a luxury. They're a necessity. So, drink up, let the water do its job, and release it from your body as often as you need to – whether it's through sweat, tears, or urination. It's all part of the process.

Water in, water out. That is the central idea of "letting it flow." Take full advantage of this fantastic liquid gift. Let yourself connect to it, be in it, and appreciate it.

What's the Bottom Line?

- About 75% of the population is chronically dehydrated

- Dehydration can lead to moodiness, fatigue, and other conditions

- By the time you're thirsty, you're already dehydrated

- Bringing water in is as important as releasing water

- Being in water is as important as taking in water

Practical Action Steps for Today...

Today, the goal is 72 ounces of water. If you're a gym rat, shoot for 96 ounces. Set a timer on your phone with reminders, keep a little notebook on hydration, and give yourself credit for your efforts.

Then make time to be in water today. Maybe get into the bathtub, into the pool, or even simply the shower today. Connect with water and see what it has to say to you.

Let's Write This! Questions to Ponder...

Part 1: Taking in water. Today the goal is to drink more water. Shoot for 72 to 96 ounces and keep track of your progress. Then make a few notes. Did you make the 8 to 10 glasses? Was it more or less? Was it easy to work it in, or was it more of a challenge than you expected? Write it all down below.

_____

_____

_____

_____

_____

_____

_____

_____

_____

_____

Part 2: Being in water. How did you choose to immerse yourself in water today? In the bathtub, in the shower, or in the ocean? How did it feel to you? What came up for you? Were there any moments of intuition or inspiration?

_____

_____

_____

_____

_____

_____

_____

_____

_____

Part 3: What does water means to you? After today's exercise, what did you realize about your connection with water? Pay attention to that relationship. What does it say to you?

_____

_____

_____

_____

_____

_____

_____

_____

_____

_____

DAY 14: FUNCTIONALITY OVER PHYSICALITY (HOW IT WORKS VS. HOW IT LOOKS)

You might've heard before that your body is the most amazing thing you will ever own. Your body is a miracle, a wonderland, a brilliant machine. I'm confident you've heard it said many times. But let me ask you this: do you believe it? Have you ever taken to heart all the ways that your body shows up for you without you having to lift a finger?

If you're not convinced of all the miracles that your BFF performs on a daily basis, I'm going to see if I can change that. Take a moment, clear your mind, and read through this mind-boggling list of *Body Facts* I have found through various research over the years. Then ask yourself again whether or not you consider yourself a walking miracle.

- Your heart pumps approximately 2,000 gallons of blood every day and beats more than 100,000 times every day.

- You take around 17,000 breaths every day on average and don't need to think about a single one of them; yet if you want to stop breathing you can voluntarily hold your breath.

- Your lungs can hold up to 6 liters of air.

- Every day your body ensures that you don't get cancer by repairing DNA strands in your cells before they turn into tumors (and it does this multiple times every day.)

- Your brain doesn't stop working. It processes about 50,000 to 60,000 thoughts per day. That means up to 35 to 40 thoughts a minute.

- Cells in your stomach lining produce an alkaline substance every few milliseconds to neutralize stomach acid. If they didn't, your stomach acid would digest your stomach itself.

- You blink about 28,000 times a day, with each one lasting a tenth of a second. This is a voluntary reflex that the body uses to keep the eyes clean and moist.

- Your eyes can size up any visual scene in just 0.01 seconds.

- Your body produces the same amount of heat as 25 lightbulbs over the course of a single day.

- Red blood cells shoot around your body, taking less than 60 seconds to complete a full circuit. That means each of them makes 1,440 trips around your body every day, delivering oxygen and keeping your body energized.

- You shed more than one million skin cells every single day, but they're automatically replenished without you having to think about it. In fact, your skin is the largest organ that you own, with a surface area of 18 square feet. That's two square meters.

- Your hair grows about half a millimeter per day. The average adult with a full scalp has about 100,000 hairs on their head. So that's a combined total of 50 meters of hair growth every single day.

- Your brain and your mouth work together to allow you to speak an average of 2,000 to 5,000 words per day.

- The glands in your mouth produce an incredible 1.5 liters of saliva every day. If this didn't happen, your mouth would become overrun with bacteria, and you wouldn't be able to digest your food.

- Each of your kidneys contains one million tiny filters that filter an average of 2.2 pints of blood every minute. That's 3,168 pints every single day, despite each kidney being only the size of a fist.

- Your hard-working kidneys also expel an average of 2.5 pints of urine from your body every day.

- The average male's testicles manufacture 10 million sperm every day. Those that aren't used will age and are eventually broken down inside the body, with any useful nutrients being absorbed and put to use.

- You grow 8 millimeters every night when you're sleeping before shrinking back down each day.

- Your body's cells are regenerating themselves every single day without any prompting. This means that you have an entirely new set of taste buds every ten days, new fingernails every 6-10 months, new bones every ten years, and even a new heart every 20 years.

If you didn't believe that your body was a work of pure genius before, I sincerely hope that you're starting to entertain that notion now. Think of all the things that your body can do. Think of all the ways it keeps everything humming with or without your help. It's performing incredible feats of endurance and protection at every moment of every day. And it never takes a single moment off. That in itself is nothing short of astounding.

But so frequently, all we focus on is that our body is beginning to creak. It's getting fat. It's not fast enough, strong enough, or pretty enough to make us happy. Therefore, it's just not good enough.

We focus on scars and call them ugly. We focus on our hips and complain that they're too big. We look at the number on the scale, and if we don't like it, we blame our bodies. Now, this is not to say that there might not be some things that you'd like to adjust so that your outer self matches your inner self. But no matter what it looks like on the outside, your BFF shows up for you. It's checking everything off of that body "to-do" list that I shared with you above ... and a whole lot more.

Whether you appreciate it or not, your body is taking care of you. It's keeping everything going so that your Spirit can experience this life in the physical world. That in itself is fricking miraculous, isn't it? Too bad that more often than not, we choose to focus on whether or not we look hot in a bikini instead of acknowledging that our heart is still beating strongly.

In other words, we put too much attention on the sheer physicality of our bodies while losing sight of the phenomenal functionality of our bodies. Each time you berate yourself for not being a perfect size you negate the miracles that your body performs for you in every single moment. You bring the energy of criticism and guilt into your body, most of the time closing the door behind it and trapping it inside. Like we talked about before, once that energy gets inside, it tends to stay there. It creates a story of its own. And eventually, it manifests in our body as pain, illness, or chronic disease.

What if you decided to stop telling the story of disease, fat, or ugly? What if you stopped dwelling on the things that don't look the way that you want them to, and started celebrating the things that function like clockwork?

Let's say that you chose to focus on the way that you want to feel rather than the way that you didn't. What would happen to the way your body manifests itself if feeling good was the goal? As we noted in the Body Facts list above, your body re-creates its cells whether we ask it to or not. The question becomes this: what are we re-creating our cells to be? Is it based on feeling light and energetic, or feeling low and fatigued? Is our body re-creating itself based on the old story or the new?

Like we talked about on "Body Story" day, your outer world does not change until your inner world does. If you have the same old thoughts, you tell the same old stories. You recognize your genetics as a life sentence and diseases associated with them as the punishment. It turns out that if you keep using the recipe for meatloaf, you're going to keep getting meatloaf. Same story, same results.

But what if you genuinely recognized that your body was a freaking miracle, and started to see it as such on an everyday basis? What if you fully appreciated everything that is working like clockwork instead of the few things that don't look like you think they should? What's the least that would happen? You'd start to feel more grateful and appreciative. Maybe even more energetic and revitalized.

Think of it this way: if your thoughts dictate how your body creates itself, how amazing would it be to build it with thoughts of love, appreciation, and support? How would that change your physical experience, and what wonders would that work for your Mind, Body, and Spirit connection? What if you could continue to rebuild your body based on the new blueprint? If your cells can physically create a new heart every 20 years, how much more amazing would that heart be if it was designed with the energy of gratitude?

It makes you wonder if when your Mind, Body, and Spirit are working together, it just might have the power not only to build the body that you dream about, but also heal nearly any physical condition.

Your body is an absolute phenomenon. It keeps on keeping on whether it has your support or not. Just imagine what it could do for you if you decided to be on its side ALL the time! Imagine what would happen if you choose to be kind and compassionate instead of angry and critical. Just think how your body could support you if you nourished it physically, mentally, emotionally, and spiritually every single day. You'd be more than a miracle – you'd be a miracle on high-vibe steroids.

My personal experience with changing focus has been a long journey. You know by now that most of my life I was one big walking mass of body issues. I didn't look the way I wanted to look. My body was not showing up the way I thought it should, and I was not feeling grateful for anything it was doing. Even though somehow I knew I was letting myself down, I kept on believing that my body was my worst enemy.

There were times when Spirit tried to intervene. It always told me, "Focus on the functionality, not the physicality, Sunny." Now, I did understand the meaning of the words well enough. But for the longest time, I wasn't buying it. Not that I didn't try to be grateful that my body was keeping me alive, of course. I attempted to focus on the positive. I could walk, I could talk, I could breathe. But my cynical thoughts always butt back in at that point. I wasn't the perfect weight or the ideal size, so who cared if my heart was beating and my lungs still functioned?

Eventually, though, my body started to give me plenty of good reasons to remember just how vital functionality was. I'd ignored its needs for too long, and I left it no choice. My body started pushing back in the form of health issues. Osteopenia. Parasites. And near-death experiences caused by infections. I began to understand that there was something to this functionality thing and that I'd better start taking it seriously.
It was time to do some mirror work. And we're talking not so much the Louise Hay kind of mirror work that involves looking into your own eyes and repeating, "I love you." It was more about learning to love the physical expression of myself. I got in front of a full-length mirror, took a deep breath, and observed how I felt about each part of my body, one piece at a time.

Some parts I had some lingering emotion around, like my feet (as you might recall, I've battled feet image issues over the years). There were other areas that I had no emotion about one way or the other, like my elbows, shoulders, or ears. Nevertheless, I took an honest look at every part of my body and asked myself how I felt at each stop. Once I'd covered the feelings for every part, there was a second step. I had to find an appreciation for how each part of my body supported me. That is, turning my attention to how each part of my body *functioned* rather than how I felt about it.

For example, I looked at my toes. At first, I didn't find very much to like about them. They sort of "kissed" at the top. They turned a strange way and had a weird shape. That was my immediate feeling. But then I also considered what they did for me every day. They helped me stay balanced when I walked. They supported me so that I could move through the world with ease. Same for my dreaded feet. Never mind that I always considered them ugly. They helped me move through life and do what I needed to do every day.

Now, this was a body evaluation that even I might like!

From there, I went up and throughout my entire body. My calves, my shins, my knees, my thighs, my vagina, my uterus, basically every body part I could name. I felt my feelings, and then I focused on the functionality. And I gave each part of my body the appreciation it deserved for helping me function every day.

I appreciated my brain for giving me the ability to think and to remember. I thanked my eyes for allowing me to take in all the beauty in the world and to recognize light and dark. I thanked my heart for continuing to beat and my lungs for bringing me all the oxygen I needed. Then something interesting happened. I noticed that the more grateful I was that my body functioned properly, the less I worried about how my belly, my chest, or my thighs looked.

Now, I'm not saying that I magically transformed my attitude about my entire body in one fell swoop. But over time and with consistent practice, my thoughts changed. My feelings changed. And I started to see my body for the miracle that it was.

I also noticed just how harmful that my thoughts could be to what was a pretty damn well-oiled machine. I fully understood that my body kept working for me despite how poorly I treated it in return. Despite all of my resistance and attitude, my body was running remarkably well. Now it was time to see how well it would run if it had all of the nurturing, compassion and positive affirmations that it needed.

The funny thing is that I knew all of this in theory at a very young age. It's just that I didn't take it all that seriously. I believed that it might work for some people, but not for me. So, I didn't practice consistently. Now, awareness is essential. But eventually, it has to lead to doing. Without taking consistent inspired action, all the good ideas in the world won't manifest into physical reality. Today, I want you to not only become aware of how your body supports you but also to start taking big action to love your body back.

How do you start appreciating how well your body works for you? Just get started. Look at the body part that you like the least right now. Whether it's something that gives you a gut-punch to look at or something that just makes you say, "Yeah, that could use some work." Look at it. Be honest with yourself about how you feel about it (without any judgment for how you feel), and then ask yourself how that same body part serves you. (Because I can guarantee that it does something for you!)

Take my butt, for example. It's always been one of my least favorite body parts. To tell you the truth, it used to be in a "happy face" kind of shape. Now it's more like a neutral face. I'd love to be able to hit the gym enough to make it "smile" again. But for now, I still love it. After all, your butt does serve a particular function, and it might not be what you think. And I've got a story to prove it.

My team and I were on a business trip to Las Vegas a few years back. Once we'd concluded our business for the day, we decided to hit the town and went dancing at Toby Keith's bar. So, there I was country dancing with a stranger. Right in the middle of a spin, my random dance partner dropped me flat on the floor. And I fell right on my butt. Of course, I jumped right back up again and finished the song, then went and found the rest of my party. As I found my way to a chair, I gingerly took my seat and said to my girls, "That's gonna hurt tomorrow!"

It turns out that I couldn't have been more right. The next day I was in excruciating pain, and I'm pretty sure it was because I broke my tailbone. I have to say that I never had more appreciation for a little bit of extra padding on my backside than I did that morning. Before that happened, I never would've thought that my butt offered anything other than how it looked in a pair of tight jeans. But as it happened, that extra cushion was a godsend while I was healing. I had just enough buffer on my backside to help keep my tailbone protected and help me function during the healing process. Functionality carried the day on that one, for sure.

Every day throughout this challenge I've asked you to focus on the things that you appreciate about your body. Today I want you to take that appreciation to a whole new place. It's time to go deeper into all of your body parts. It's time to be honest about how you feel about them and release any negative emotions that need to go. Then shift your feelings away from how things look and find a deep sense of gratitude for how well things work.

What's the Bottom Line?

- Your body is supporting you 24/7 whether you are aware of it or not

- It keeps you alive even without your appreciation

- Think of how much more it could help you if it had your love and gratitude

- The more you focus on how your body supports you, the less critical its appearance becomes

- If your body re-creates itself based on thoughts, choose the best thoughts for your blueprint

Practical Action Steps for Today...

First, take a few moments and review the Body Facts I shared with you at the beginning of this lesson. After you've gotten through this section and entertained some new ideas, doesn't everything on that list seem even more amazing? Keep that in mind as you move along to the second task for today.

Second, spend some time focusing on how your body works for you. You can start at the top or the bottom. Scan your body and focus on all of the areas. How does each part of your body support you? Allow yourself to experience your feelings too, but then shift to the function. Do this full-body scan twice today and notice what comes up for you. Look at your feelings about each body part first. Then shift to its function. Whether you appreciate how a particular body part looks or not right now, notice how that part serves you today.

The more you appreciate how your physical container supports you, the easier it is to acknowledge the miracle that you are.

Let's Write This! Questions to Ponder...

Part 1: Review the Body Facts and allow yourself to be amazed. Before you dive into today's homework, take a few moments to look at the Body Facts list at the beginning of this lesson. After reading today's section, do you have a new perspective on how much your body supports you? What fact on that list is the most amazing and miraculous to you? Write down a few of your impressions right here.

_____

_____

_____

_____

_____

Part 2: Scan your body. Start at the top or the bottom. Scan through your fantastic body and consider each part. How do you feel about each body part? Be honest and allow whatever comes up to surface completely. Then for each body part, consider just how it supports you. What does it do that makes your everyday life easier? How does each one help you? Remember to do this exercise twice today, perhaps in the morning and the evening. Then make a few notes below.

_____

_____

_____

_____

How do you feel about each part of your body? List each part and the feelings that come up.

_____

_____

_____

_____

_____

How does each part of your body support you? List each part and add at least one essential function it performs for you.

_____

_____

_____

_____

_____

Part 3: Body function aha's and epiphanies. After you complete today's exercise, make a few notes about what you noticed. Did you have any shifts in energy or attitude? No matter how big or how small, make sure to include any changes or aha's you experienced today.

_____

_____

_____

_____

_____

DAY 15: LET'S MOVE!
PUTTING THE BODY IN MIND-BODY-SPIRIT

We've been focusing a lot on inner work over the past few days. Of course, everything begins on the inside. That's why we've taken the time to explore your thoughts, feelings, and emotions before focusing on the outer expression of your being. You've created a new body story. You've learned to listen and respond to what your body is telling you. And you've learned to appreciate your body's functionality over everything else.

Now, it's time to let that body take center stage. It's time to use your body for what it was made to do. And everybody's body was made to MOVE.

Today is all about moving that body, in whatever way it needs you to. Whether that's walking, dancing, yoga, or a trip to the gym. It doesn't matter how physically fit you think you are (or are not). Everyone can move in some way. So, you're going to move that body, stir up that energy, and bring the Mind, Body, and Spirit together in a whole new way.

Now, full disclosure here. I believe in wellness, and I make alignment in the Mind, Body, and Spirit a priority. But at the same time, I've never really been much of a workout girl. In fact, it's probably been a good 15 or so years since I've followed any sort of fitness regimen that most people would recognize.

It probably won't surprise you that up until now, my attention has primarily been on the energetic and vibrational side of life. I've been a champion of the emotional, spiritual, and mental components of the human experience. But as far as the physical fitness part? Not so much. That's probably because for so many years, all I ever focused on was my body. And not in a loving and nurturing way, if you recall the stories I have shared with you.

When I shifted my concentration to my mind and Spirit, I have to say that working out took a back seat. I went from obsessively exercising in hopes of changing my body to focusing pretty exclusively on the spiritual side of life.

Of course, it wasn't like I was neglecting my body. When I was called to move, I moved. I went for walks, I loved to swim, and when my family and I went on vacation, I'd go for hikes. I was more than reasonably active this whole time. I felt healthy and stable for the most part. I wasn't getting sick the way I used to. I figured that my physical health was taking care of itself.

Over the last 15 years or so, my priority had been energy work, emotional healing, and spiritual alignment. An actual at-the-gym, work-up a sweat exercise routine hadn't been part of the picture for a long time.

All that changed on the morning of October 15th, 2016.

It was a Monday morning. I was lying in bed, greeting a new day and preparing to begin my daily meditation practice, when out of the blue I received a laser-specific message. Spirit spoke to me, and its words were clear as a bell.

"Go work out."

No further explanation. No additional comments or instructions. But there was no mistaking what the message was. "Go work out."

Now, for someone who hadn't seen the inside of a gym in 15 years, that was a pretty unlikely directive to receive. But I'd heard that voice before. It was the same one that told me that I had the power to heal myself. It was the same one that said, "No more iced tea." That voice wasn't messing around. I knew I'd better follow my marching orders.

I said to my husband, "Let's go to the gym." He gave me a look back as if to say, "Who are you and where is my wife?" I admitted it was a weird thing for me to suggest. But I also knew that there was no refusing the call that morning. We headed out to the gym adjacent to our home. I did my workout and fulfilled my obligations.

At the time, I figured that this would be a one-time stint. I didn't think it was going to become part of the daily to-dos. But the next morning, my Spirit was back at it. There that message was again. "Go work out."

This time I thought to myself, "Really? I worked out yesterday. I've got shit to do. I've got a life to live. I'm busy." Carving out more time for a workout every day didn't seem doable. My day was jammed-packed enough as it was. How long was this Spirit-ordered fitness kick supposed to continue?

But again, the voice was not to be ignored. It was the voice of my Spirit. It was my Soul's wisdom telling me to listen up and listen good. So, my husband and I hit the gym. Again.

Before I knew it, gym time became a daily thing. By the time Friday rolled around, I was telling my girls at our weekly team meeting that I'd been working out every day this past week. And I got some pretty flabbergasted looks. My girls know me well, and naturally, their response was, "You're working out?" I answered that Spirit told me on Monday that I needed to exercise, so I did. Naturally, the next question on their minds (as well as mine) was, "Why?"

Honestly, I didn't know. Maybe I needed to get healthier. There might've been something going on in my body that I needed to move out before it turned into a health issue. The only clue I had was that along with the instruction to exercise, I also heard the word "strength." Spirit was telling me that I needed to gain more physical strength. But it didn't say why. I know, I'm a psychic medium and maybe I "should've" known. But even we have to have our own life experiences, so we don't see it all.

Then three weeks later, here in the U.S. we had the presidential election. As you know, Donald Trump came out the winner. When I woke up that morning after the news had broken, I discovered that my community was falling to pieces. We're talking flipping out in ways that I considered unhealthy. There was a lot of fear, anger, and blame flying around on both sides of the political aisle.

I'm not calling out one side or another, and I'm not making any political statements with this story. All I'm doing is reporting what I found in the aftermath of that event. And what I found was that in just about every way, the energy shifted to a significant low in my community ... and the vibration of the country plummeted right along with it.

At that moment, my head began making some rationalizations. I needed to get physically stronger so that I'd have the strength to help my community move through the fear and the pain. It seemed that I needed to hold more space for people, and my body just needed to be stronger, so that was why Spirit insisted that I hit the gym. Made sense, right?

Over the next several months, the workout routine continued. I kept on exercising, walking, and moving. We even got bicycles. The physical fitness kick continued bigtime. Sometimes I worked out two to three times in a single day.

A few months later in March, my team and I were in Palm Springs preparing to teach a business mentoring course when I received a phone call. I learned that one of my dearest clients was killed in a car accident. That was heartbreaking enough on its own. But this particular client was also an integral part of my community. And once again, my tribe needed my strength and support in a big way. That physical power I'd been cultivating over the last several months helped me carry the day once again.

It turns out that this wasn't all. Over the next two and a half months, between my community and my family, we had eight deaths. My aunt died, my cousin's husband passed away, we lost a very close colleague, and several of my students died over that two-month span. Eight deaths in 10 weeks. Most of them were unexpected, too.

The more that the situation deepened, the more awareness I received. I needed strength in all ways: energetically, emotionally, vibrationally, and physically. Had I not built my physical strength starting with that initial directive from Spirit, I wouldn't have been able to hold the energetic space to support my tribe. Nor would I have had the strength to take care of me properly.

So today, we're going to focus on moving your body. It's about bringing that physical component into your Mind-Body-Spirit practice. Most of the time when you think of working out, I bet that losing weight is the top priority. But that's not what I'm talking about here. The idea is to build the strength so that your body can carry you through life with ease and grace. It's about being ready and able to move through anything that life throws your way.

We're not talking about improving the way that you look. It's about creating a healthy and robust container to carry you through this life journey. You could call it the ultimate expression of functionality over physicality.

It starts with taking the time for movement. And doing it consistently.

No matter who you are, where you are, or what your situation is, there are ways to work movement into your life. Even if it's nothing more than walking around your house, that counts! (Robin, one of the girls on my team, says that she gets 5,000 steps a day just doing her laundry.) You don't need an expensive gym or a complicated regimen to get the results that you need. All you need to do is to move every day, and each day make it a little bit more than you did the day before.

Sometimes people say, "No pain, no gain." Now, I don't think that pain needs to be your mantra. But I think that what you do should stretch you a little bit. You don't necessarily need to push yourself to exhaustion in the weight room or at the running track. But if your exercise routine isn't making you "feel the burn" at all, it's time to raise the bar just a little bit.

A while back, my team and I went rock climbing. When I was scaling the wall, I felt that burn in my upper body like I hadn't in a long time. But the next day, I didn't have any soreness at all. That meant that there was probably room for me to push a little bit more than I did that day. See, it's not excruciating next-day soreness that you need. Just a little indication that you pushed yourself beyond your comfort zone.

That's what we're going for today: expanding your comfort zone spiritually, mentally, emotionally, AND physically.

It could be anything, just as long as it's more than you did yesterday. You can incorporate movement into your day in a lot of ways, too. It doesn't have to be as formal as a trip to the gym. It could be as simple as a walk. You could take the stairs instead of the elevator. Or choose a parking spot farther away from your destination to get in a few extra steps. Just move your body and stretch just beyond what you usually do.

Start with assessing the physical activity you get on a daily or weekly basis and raise the bar just a little bit today. Either raise the bar or change it up, whatever feels like a stretch to you. If you usually walk three miles, take it up to 3.2. If you regularly hit the elliptical, try a spin class instead. If you're devoted to the treadmill, add an extra level of incline. Today is about changing things up and pushing ahead. If you're comfortable with what you're doing, that means that you've mastered it. And it's time to take it to the next level, even if that is only one more step.

So, let's move that beautiful, amazing, miraculous rock-star body of yours. Let's show your BFF how much you love and honor it. And know that it is right there with you and ready to move to the next level.

It doesn't matter what you do, as long as it takes you one step further than you are right now. So, pick your activity and commit to it right now. Decide to show up for yourself for at least 15 minutes. If you can swing it, go for 30 minutes. But 15 minutes, bare minimum. I know you've got that in you.

One thing to remember, too. Today isn't about "getting in shape" or losing weight. It isn't about crushing it in the gym to prove yourself a worthy human being. It's not about forcing your body to look a certain way. It's about honoring your body and building your strength. It's about creating your power mentally, emotionally, spiritually, and physically. In the end, all those components matter equally. That's the whole point of Mind-Body-Spirit.

What's the Bottom Line?

- Physical strength isn't about how your body looks

- Honor your body and allow it to support you

- Building physical strength is as essential as energetic strength

- Pain isn't necessary to build strength, but you do need to stretch yourself

Practical Action Steps for Today...

Right here, right now, decide how you're going to move your body today and write it down. Give yourself some accountability as well. Maybe that's telling a friend to hold you to your promise. It might even be sharing your workout plans on your Facebook page and asking your friends to keep you honest about it. But most importantly, choose something that'll give you 15 to 30 minutes of movement, write it down, and most importantly, do it.

All I'm asking for is a little bit beyond your typical physical routine. If that means adding a quarter of a mile to your run, do it. Then again, if for you that means walking to your mailbox and back, that works for me. Even if you're traveling, you can still work some movement into your day. If you have physical limitations, there's something you can do to get yourself moving. I don't care how big or how small your activity is. All it needs to be is a bit of a stretch for you.

Let's Write This! Questions to Ponder...

Part 1: How are you going to move your body today? Write down what you're going to do for yourself today. How are you going to show up for yourself and move your body? Write it down right here.

_____

_____

_____

_____

_____

_____

_____

Part 2: How did it feel to stretch yourself? How far beyond your "normal" did you go today, and how did it feel? Was it liberating, inspiring, discouraging, tiring, or a combination of several emotions? Write down what came up for you right here.

_____

_____

_____

_____

_____

_____

_____

Part 3: Give yourself credit ... and keep going! You've stretched yourself just a little bit further than usual. Now give yourself credit for it! Give yourself a note of appreciation for honoring your commitment to yourself. Let your BFF thank you for fulfilling the promise that you made to it. And then, create a plan to keep that forward motion going.

Write yourself a note of appreciation and encouragement right here:

_____

_____

_____

_____

_____

_____

_____

_____

_____

Then, commit to keeping it going! What are you going to do to move your body for the next week? Write it down right here, then make it happen.

_____

_____

_____

_____

_____

_____

_____

_____

_____

DAY 16: PICTURES AND PERSPECTIVE

Pictures. Photographs. Moments in time. For a lot of us, pictures are a pretty emotionally-charged topic. It goes to a whole new level when it comes to seeing our own reflections.

When you catch a look at yourself in a picture, how does it make you feel? It's true: photos can be a pretty emotionally-charged topic. How many times do you hear somebody say, "I LOVE the way I look in pictures?" It's pretty much one of those, "said no one ever" kind of things, isn't it?

But what if you could look at pictures of yourself from the past and the present and not only make peace with what you see, but also see something you might've missed before?

Today I'm inviting you to open up your photo album and see what is really behind the smiles.

I'm talking about looking closer. Seeing something beyond what the actual photo portrays. Pictures catch moments in time, but they also capture the feeling and the energy of that time and space. It's up to you what you take from it when you see it.

How do you feel when you see pictures of yourself? Does it make you catch your breath? The key here is to bring awareness to your feelings and experiences as you look at an earlier version of you. That energy that comes up can go a lot of different directions, after all. Some people look at old photos of themselves and see a person they don't even recognize. Others see themselves and think, "Wow, I look a lot better than I thought!" Then again, many of us pick apart and magnify every unsavory detail.

Sometimes, though, I bet you see even more in the pictures you keep. Ever seen an old snapshot and not recall where it was taken or what you were doing, because all that stands out are the feelings behind the smile?

In other words, your face might have been smiling, but your heart might've felt something else entirely.

Pictures capture the energy and the mood of a moment in time. But the energy and the spirit might not necessarily be reflected in what meets the eye. Sometimes we smile to hide our feelings. Or maybe stand behind someone or something else. There are moments where we're so afraid of how we're going to look after the camera snaps, that we miss out on the experience of the moment. And unfortunately, those feelings of guilt, shame, or self-consciousness are all that we remember. Sometimes it's all too easy to get stuck in the way we perceive ourselves, so that we miss out on a once-in-a-lifetime experience.

In other words, some moments and experiences look idyllic in a photograph. But when you look back on them, all you remember are the guilt, anger, or shame you were feeling - either about yourself or about the situation.

But the good news is that you can choose how you want to feel about anything ... including the pieces of time that are captured by the camera. Today is all about looking at pictures of yourself and seeing them with new eyes. I'm not talking about revising history, here. All I'm inviting you to do is to look closer, understand more deeply, and give yourself the gift of a new perspective on an old picture. You might be surprised – and pleased – by what you see.

I have very few pictures of myself as a teenager. Maybe one or two survived through the years. At the time, like many of us, I would hide from the camera as much as I could. Hard to believe it if you know me now, but it's true. Even after I started releasing physical weight, I didn't consider my body beautiful. I fixated on my body weight no matter what my size was. In fact, in every picture of myself as a teenager and as a young adult, I could look at it and tell you exactly what I weighed.

No matter where I was, what was going on in my life, or what I was doing, my happiness was based solely on how I looked. What I knew for sure was that how I looked on the outside in no way agreed with how I looked on the inside. I usually put on a cute smile to cover up a lot of pain, judgment, and self-criticism.

Can you relate? I'm willing to bet that sounds at least a little bit familiar to you. That's part of the reason why pictures can be such an emotional minefield for so many of us. But that's also why I'm asking you to look at them today. Because if you can look at yourself, drop the judgment, and see what is happening "behind the scenes," you might be amazed at what is there. You might see how far you've come and how much you've learned. You might find truth and beauty that you never imagined possible.

I'm going to help you get the journey started by sharing some of my photographic memories. I'll share a bit of the back story and the circumstances. And I'll also tell you what I remember feeling when that picture was taken. That part might surprise you. The point is, that things are not always as they seem ... and what you see on the outside hardly tells the whole story.

This picture was taken when I was 15 years old. At the time I had already quit school and had yet to go to a high school dance. My friend Shelly's school was hosting a Sadie Hawkins dance, and she asked me to come along and bring a guest of my own. I invited a close guy friend to be my date, and this was the picture we took.

I was 15 and weighed about 40 pounds more than most girls my age. My friend Shelly was a cute, petite little thing, while I was oversized and chubby. What was even more unnerving for me was that we had a pool party before the dance. Naturally, the first thing that I got wound up about was getting into a swimsuit in front of other people. I was putting a damper on my evening before it even began.

In the end, I did get in the pool. But when I look at this picture, what I remember is that the entire experience was embarrassing. I was mortified about how I looked in that bathing suit. I was convinced that nobody would find me attractive because of the fat rolls I was sure I had. I barely ate anything because I didn't want to feel more overweight than I already felt.

It was my first and only high school dance. There was a smile on my face in this picture. But the smile hid all the turmoil that was going on inside.

This picture was taken when I was at my highest weight. For years, every time I saw this shot, I would feel myself shrinking inside. I remember how sad this girl was. Here was a girl who was so busy comparing herself to everybody else that she was never able to see her beauty. When I look at her now, I recognize the girl who taught me so much about the woman I am now. She taught me about my value and my worth. But when I see her I also see the sadness, the hiding, and the layers of pain.

Now, this picture was taken after I had my first son and started to release weight. It was the year that I met my husband, and we were on a trip to Mexico together. As you can see, I'm a bit thinner in this picture, but there's one thing I specifically remember about this picture when it was taken. I was holding in my stomach and saying to myself, "hurry up, take the picture now!" I didn't want the picture taken with even a hint of a fat roll, and I was afraid I could only suck in my gut so much.

That, of all things, was what I remembered from my first vacation with my future husband … The worry that I wouldn't look skinny in the pictures. The hope that I could suck my stomach in long enough to not look fat.

Of course, everything looks happy and hunky-dory on the outside, doesn't it?

Here's a picture that was taken at my son's 4th birthday party. I was around 110 pounds at the time. But the skirt I was wearing felt tighter than I thought it should. And for the rest of the day, I couldn't forget that. So, there I was at my son's birthday party, and instead of enjoying the moment with him, all I thought about was what I couldn't eat. Sure, I was there. I was paying attention to my son and playing the gracious hostess. I was physically there. But I wasn't *present.* I was secretly obsessing over my weight and focused on forbidden food rather than celebrating my own child's birthday. And you'd never know that just by looking at our smiling faces, would you?

(And yes, when I first saw these pictures, my first thought was relief that my stomach wasn't sticking out.)

Now, this picture was taken on my wedding day. My husband and I got married in November in Sedona, and this was my version of a wedding dress. (Non-traditional doesn't begin to describe it, right?) Here was the bride, in jeans and cowboy boots.

It was a beautiful ceremony, but that wasn't the first memory that this picture calls back. You see, the jeans I was wearing were size 7. I needed a size nine at the time, but I pushed my way into the jeans I thought should fit me.

It was my wedding day. But all day long, all I thought about was how fat I was ... and how I felt that I had to wear a coat over my clothes to cover it up. I barely ate anything the night before so that I wouldn't feel fat on my wedding day. But I felt fat anyway.

Not quite how you'd want to remember the happiest day of your life, right?

These pictures were all taken during my teens up through my mid-20s. But in the last 15 or so years, I've experienced some significant shifts. I've been more open to and able to embrace myself, as I am. I've learned to love the person I am on the inside without obsessing about how I looked on the outside. Most of all, I've let go of the worry. Now I see myself as a healthy, fit, kind and strong woman rather than drowning in fear about what I could and couldn't eat. I was no longer defined by my physical body. And nothing has been more liberating.

Have a look at a few of these snapshots in time.

This photo was taken about seven years ago in San Diego. I was on a day trip to the beach with my son, and I remember having a fantastic time. I couldn't tell you what I weighed at the time. There's nothing more going on than what you see there. The calmness and serenity reflected on the outside perfectly matched the vibe on the inside.

This picture was taken at *Celebrate Your Life,* and it's one of my favorite pictures. I was dressed to the nines, of course, but there was more to it than that. What I love about this moment is the confidence I had. I was in my Spirit and was doing my divine work. I felt aligned, empowered, and strong. I felt the connection to Spirit and knew that I was genuinely being heard for the person I was. And that is what comes across the most for me in this picture.

In the last picture, I was all dressed up and made up perfectly. In this one, I'm just wearing comfy sweatpants and a sweatshirt. And you know what? I love this picture just as much as the last one. I was just as connected, aligned, and in the moment here as I was in the previous shot. The energy and the connection of the moment says it all.

But how many times do you see yourself in pictures and think that you look like shit, only to tear it up or delete it from your phone or camera? Or how many times do you not even allow yourself to be photographed because you don't want to be seen at all?

When I went back through these pictures, I have to admit I was a little bit shocked with myself. I mean, seriously, I missed my son's birthday celebration because I was so damn worried about whether I could eat a piece of pizza or not. I missed out on the full experience of my wedding day because I was busy chastising myself for not looking or feeling the way that I thought I should.

I was obsessing about food. Obsessing about not being good enough or not looking right … all while these amazing life experiences were happening right in front of me. How much of my life did I miss because I focused on the things that I had decided were true in my head? The thing with pictures, though, is that you'll see what you need to see. You'll perceive what you choose to focus on. Whether you focus on your acne or your hairstyle, or you focus on whether or not you have makeup on, or whether you focus on how fat you think you are, pictures will capture whatever you choose to look at.

Maybe it's time that we choose to focus on something other than what we've seen all this time.

What if you decided to look at a picture and remember the experience you had, who you were with, and what you did ... rather than how you think you looked? I know I've been able to change my perspective on old photographs. And you can too.

Maybe it's time to start going through your pictures and start seeing them for what they are: a moment captured in time ... of a spiritual being, having a physical experience. Maybe it's also time to start taking some new pictures and include yourself in the moment, too. And start seeing yourself in new pictures having a fantastic time instead of focusing exclusively on how you think you should look.

What do I mean? First of all, let's talk about old pictures.
So, is it time to take some of those pictures out and look for something different? I could see photos from my trip to Mexico and say, "that's a girl who is obsessing about her body and hasn't eaten anything all day because she didn't want to feel fat." Or I could look at the same picture and say, "well that's a pretty thin girl by the beach." Both statements are true. But which one would I rather see?

Second, what if you could decide to see the person who you are today in a loving, kind, and nurturing way – even in pictures? Maybe all of those landscape pictures that you take could include you once in a while. Maybe it would not only be amazing to capture some of your real-time human experiences in photos for yourself, but also for the people who love you. After all, your family and your friends love you as you are. They want to have memories of you for themselves, too, just as you want to have memories of the people you love.

As I said, I have very few pictures of my teenage years. I was so afraid to be seen back then that I hid from the camera. I didn't want to see myself in pictures the way I thought of myself back then. But the funny part is that hiding from the camera didn't change the way I looked. It didn't make me lose 40 pounds or bring on a surge of empowerment. Hiding just made me feel more ashamed.

Now, in the place that I am today, I wish I had more pictures from back then. I wish I had more from back then to share from the perspective of where I am today. But I denied myself that by hiding.

You can probably see pretty clearly now how hiding holds you back. What's the real reason behind you pulling back? Are you hiding from other people, or hiding from yourself? Perhaps both? But what you're missing out on is your Spirit, your life force energy. It's the Spirit within that we genuinely capture in all of these pictures, if we allow it. Unfortunately, most of the time we focus so much on the physical appearance, that we miss the energy and the aura of the experience.

One of the most important things I've come to understand about pictures has been, of all things, through my experiences with death. It might sound a little bit morbid but stay with me on this one. When someone dies, what do you do? You create a celebration of their life. And you go through pictures. When my husband's best friend passed away, for instance, we noticed how few photos we had of him. And honestly, it made both me and my husband sad.

Now, I'm not necessarily saying that you better take as many pictures as you can now in case people die. That's not the point. What I am saying is that I have learned to appreciate photographs even more through loss. Because isn't that what we do when we no longer have someone with us in the physical body? We look for their physical presence in another way, and pictures are one those ways. We will all have experiences where if we haven't been taking photos, we will wish that we had.

Now, the reason I'm sharing these things isn't to bring you down or cause a sense of worry. It's simply to remind you that you don't have to hide. You don't need to be ashamed of how you look. Remember that your BFF is doing the best it can with what you've given her. When you support her more from the inside out, she'll do better from the inside out.

For today, looking at pictures is where this starts. Sure, it might bring up some painful emotions. You might feel more than a little bit vulnerable. But vulnerability is where your healing begins.

I'm not asking you to overlook the pain and sugar-coat unhappy memories. When you see your photograph, be honest when you remember what you were feeling the moment that picture was taken. But what I do hope you'll realize is that you will see whatever you choose to see. Maybe it's time to redirect your focus. I invite you to look at an old picture with a fresh perspective. What would you say to your BFF as you look back on something? Maybe it's time to be your own BFF and finally let your body off the hook.

That in itself, can be one of the greatest gifts you ever give yourself.

What's the Bottom Line?

- Pictures are simply moments in time

- They contain a million different truths

- The key is to focus on what you want to see

- You can choose to see yourself from a different perspective

- When you hide from the camera, what are you hiding from?

- Focus on the life force energy in pictures, not just physical appearances

Practical Action Steps for Today...

Today, I want you to grab a few pictures of yourself. It doesn't have to be a lot, maybe three or four. Make it a sampling of different times in your life if you can. For each image, I want you to look at it from a different perspective than you usually do. Your first thought might be what it has always been, and that's OK. Just take a look at the picture again, for a second opinion ... see if you might redirect it another way. Instead of defaulting to the usual self-deprecation and criticisms, find something that you like about the picture. Focus on the experience, the people, and the place. What was the deeper and more expansive experience? What was going on in that moment other than the initial triggers or old ideas?

Go through your old pictures and create a new story around them. Make a note of how you felt when you first saw those pictures ... and decide how you could choose to see them differently.

I'd also invite you to make a new commitment to yourself. A commitment to living and experiencing life full-out without hiding. Decide that you're no longer going to hide from an object that just captures moments in time. Realize that you don't have to fear the camera because you no longer fear who you are. Sure, maybe you're not entirely clear about *who* you are just yet. But one thing I can promise you absolutely: you're not all of the nasty things you've ever told yourself that you are. And you don't need to hide from anything. Least of all a camera.

Let's Write This! Questions to Ponder...

Part 1: Choose your photographs. Grab your set of photographs, and let's get started! For each photo that you chose, jot down a little bit about it. What are your initial feelings on each one? What is the default thought that pops up? Jot it down below.

_____

_____

_____

_____

_____

_____

_____

_____

_____

_____

_____

_____

_____

_____

_____

_____

_____

_____

_____

_____

Part 2: Change your story. Now that you know your first thought, how can you redirect the second thought? It's time to create a new story around each photograph. What do you choose to see the second time around? Focus on the people, the places, and the things going on in each picture. Most of all, focus on yourself and look beyond the obvious. Can you see and feel the life force energy behind each picture?

Create a new, more expansive, more empowering story for each picture right here.

_____

_____

_____

_____

_____

_____

_____

_____

_____

_____

_____

_____

_____

_____

_____

_____

_____

_____

_____

_____

_____

_____

_____

_____

_____

_____

_____

_____

_____

DAY 17: DECLUTTERING THE CLUTTER ("REAL" AND IMAGINED)

When you think of "clutter," the first vision you might get is a kid's messy bedroom or a grandmother's house covered floor to ceiling in dusty nick-nacks.

What does clutter entail, though? How about those things that take up space in your world, but don't give much back? I'm talking about those items that you cling to, but you don't know why. Maybe you're even clinging to things but aren't even aware that you're doing it.

Old clothes that don't fit, nick-nacks that collect dust on your shelves, or household items that don't work anymore. Sure, it might just be sitting there doing nothing. But the truth is that clutter tells a story, whether you're listening to it or not.

You see, what takes up space on the outside can give you tremendous insight into what's going on inside. And if you allow yourself to understand the secret language of junk, it might show you things in your life that need a little more love and attention.

Think of it for a moment. "Stuff" can look like just stuff ... but what if it's more like "stuffing," if you will? What if hoarding clutter is merely a form of excess protection, just like carrying extra weight can be?

You might wonder what exactly you'd need to protect yourself from. Maybe you're afraid to let go of things because you don't think you'll be able to replace them. Perhaps old junk represents a time, place, or person that you don't want to dismiss from your life.

But sometimes when you cling too much to the old, moving forward becomes a lot more of a struggle. Sometimes holding onto old clutter means blocking new energy and abundance from flowing into your life. It might even translate into self-inflicted punishment.

You can hold onto clutter in your physical space. But it also shows up in the space between your ears. Let's talk a little bit about where the clutter is in your world, and what it might be doing without you even knowing it.

What is going on in your closet right now? Have you ever held onto clothes that don't fit? Maybe it's a pair of jeans that are just a size too small ... that you're hoping you'll be able to squeeze into one day. It could be a dress that used to fit you like a glove but is a struggle to zip up anymore. What about something that is too big, but you hold onto it for fear of putting on more weight? How do you feel when you see the clothes in your closet that for whatever reason just don't fit?

Clutter isn't just in your living room, your kitchen, or your closet, either. You might have old outfits that don't suit you, but I bet there are just as many old tapes playing through your mind that are just as outdated. Clutter in your head needs to be cleared just as much as the clutter in your space.

So today the focus is clearing out the clutter. Clutter in your closet, clutter in your mind. Letting go of what doesn't serve you anymore. Let's get ready for a clean sweep of the body and mind, and of course the Spirit.

Let's start with your closet.

Take a scan of your closet and tell me what you see. What happens when that too-small skirt or pair of jeans catches your eye? Now ask yourself this: how does it make you feel? And secondly, if something doesn't fit, why does it still deserve a place in your space?

I don't know what story you might be telling yourself about misfit clothes, or even if you're telling a story at all. But one of the rationalizations I've heard the most often for holding onto tight-fitting clothes is, "I'm keeping them there to inspire me." More than likely that means "inspire me" to lose weight. And you know what I have found? Except for a very few instances, keeping clothes that don't fit is anything but inspiring. It creates comparison, judgment, and feeling overwhelmed. Most of all, that morphs into punishment. And you punish yourself every time you walk into that closet. You're exposing yourself to the guilt and shame of not being the size you think you need to be ... and there's a size whatever pair of pants in there to prove to you that you're not. That translates directly into punishment.

I've seen it too many times, and I've experienced it myself: Holding onto clothes because you think it'll inspire you to lose weight ... Holding onto outfits because you believe that you'll tend to gain weight. Whether you're keeping clothes that are too big or too small, the reason usually turns out to be one of two things. Either protection from the unknown, or punishment for not being where you wish you were. No matter what, that translates into a lack mentality.

Now, you might think that you have a valid reason for keeping what doesn't fit – that one day you'll fit into them and you won't have to repurchase them. I get that, no judgment here. But if that's your story, what's the real story behind it? Maybe it's the worry that you won't have the money to get what you need when you need it, so you better hold on to everything. You're letting that lack vibration remind you that you're not where you want to be. You might not ever be where you want to be. And this "proves" that you deserve punishment.

That lack-based mentality continues to cycle through your head. It clutters up your mental space and sets up shop. Eventually, it spills over into other areas of your life. It could be financially. "I don't have enough." It could be emotionally. "I need more." It could be personally. "I'm not enough."

Sounds like a lot to get out of a pair of pants or an old swimsuit that doesn't fit anymore, right? But the truth is, it's all connected. What shows up on the outside is simply a reflection of what's going on inside. It's not the fact that you might have stuff in your closet that doesn't fit. That in and of itself doesn't mean anything. What's important here is what energy will those misfit clothes produce? What do they make you feel? And do you want to perpetuate those feelings? That's the real question here.

The good news is that you have a choice. You can choose to keep what perpetuates the feelings you want. And let go of what stirs up the feelings that you don't want. Simple as that. Today, I'm giving you the opportunity to start re-working your closet and turning it into a haven of support and a reflection of who you are NOW.

That does not necessarily mean overhauling the entire space in 24 hours. Your closet might have taken years to get to where it is right now, and I'm not expecting you to binge-clean today. All I am asking is that you remove three to five things from your closet today. Things that bring you down more than they lift you up. Let go of three to five things that are taking up energetic space that you'd rather have back for yourself.

What kinds of things am I talking about? That depends on you. It might be an oversized or undersized piece of clothing. Then again, it could also be an old style, something that you used to love but doesn't give you a tingle anymore. It might be something that you used to wear because somebody told you that you should. Maybe it's something that makes you feel ugly and frumpy, but for whatever reason, you believe that it defines you.

Scan the energy in your closet. Notice the energy around the items in your closet. And if something is not making you happy anymore, it's time to cut the ties.

But what happens when you're afraid to let go? Maybe you do believe that if you gain or lose weight, you'll just have to replace it. But remember, vibrationally, that's a lack mentality. If we don't change the vibration of that, you set yourself up for the yo-yo. Again, make no judgment here, but just look at it with honesty. Remember, everything is energy, so if I release the energy I am holding onto, I allow new energy to come in to take its place.

What if you're holding onto something old because you're invested in comparison? It could even be the comparison to an outdated version of yourself. Or a version of yourself that you may or may not become. Either way, you're setting yourself up for failure. You are who you are at this moment. And you owe it to yourself to bring love and support to the person you are right NOW.

So, to begin, step into your closet. Take a deep breath and tune into that vibration. Let yourself pick up on the energy of that space. Then start scanning the area and take a little inventory. If you find an item that makes you feel frumpy, consider pulling the plug. If there's something that you're clinging to for when you're a "perfect" size six, but right now all it's doing is tormenting you, toss it in the "Let It Go" box. If you're looking at a dress you wore in high school that makes you cringe when you see it, Goodwill, here we come.

That's the first part of today's exercise, clearing the clutter out of the physical space. The second part is considering the clutter in your mind. Just like in your closet, there's a lot of old thoughts, ideas, and patterns living in your head that could stand to be swept away. No matter who you are, there are thoughts on a repeating loop in your head that don't serve you. What's more, the greater the repetition of those cluttered ideas on the inside, the more they're likely to manifest on the outside. And they need to go just as much as the shirt in your closet that is two sizes too small.

Now, you can't reach into your head, pull out a negative thought and chuck it in a box for the thrift shop. For that matter, how do you recognize a cluttered idea in the first place?

Here's the deal: *cluttered thoughts are thoughts that don't support what you desire to create in your life.* They're the ideas that work against you, rather than for you, when you imagine your dream life. And whether or not you're aware of it, they might be wreaking havoc and pushing away the very things you've been desperate to manifest all these years. I want to help you put a stop to it, right now.

So just as you did with your closet, allow yourself to do a little scan on your mind. All you have to do is simply pay attention to what is going on in your head today. From there, just like with your closet, identify three to five thoughts that don't serve the life you desire to create. And when you catch them, simply write them down.

When you find the thoughts that you're ready to release, pay attention to them when they come up. Each time they push their way into your mind, instead of denying them or pushing them down, bring them up. Bring awareness to them. Then tell them, "thank you for sharing, but I'm not interested. I'm not focusing there anymore." Then replace them with a new affirmation.

Write down your cluttering thoughts of choice in one column. Then on the other side, write down the opposite idea. Pivot the thought to create a positive affirmation that feels good and true to you, one that shifts you out of the negative version that has been playing in your head for years.

Then, when those old thoughts next show up, thank them for sharing, tell them you're not interested, and that you choose to focus on something else. Then bring in your new affirmation as a replacement. Use it early and often – out with the old, in with the new!

The idea is to remove three to five un-supporting thoughts that take up too much bandwidth in your brain. And free up that space for the greatness you dream of creating.

So, let's get back to the closet for a little while. I have a lot of clothes. Maybe you do too. I happen to like clothes, as I think they're a fun way to express myself. Some outfits I've had for at least 15 years. All of my clothes still fit, but a lot of them don't quite vibe with me anymore. That's another reason to let something go. If it's a style that represents an outdated version of you, someone you used to be but just aren't anymore, it's going to be an energetic drag. That's another area that you can declutter.

But whether it represents a style, a size, or a vibe that's not working for you, it's time to move it. If it's something that you know you won't wear because it's worn out, it's time to send it back out into the Universe.

If you're on the fence about letting something go, here's a quick check-in you can do for yourself: Let's say you try on pants that don't fit. *How does it make you feel?* Maybe it's guilty or ashamed that you can't get them zipped up. Perhaps it's fearful that you might gain even more weight. Those are the kind of feelings that bring you down, and they're clues that it might be useful to release this item.

Again, I'm not asking you to go through your entire closet in a single day. Pick out 3-5 items – or more than that, if you feel like it – but don't feel obligated. You can make it just a few for today and take the process in small steps at a time.

As you go along, keep a few questions in mind. When you're making your selections for the chopping block, ask yourself why you chose what you chose. What did these items represent for you? And how did it feel to let them go? You might feel relief. Maybe concern or fear might creep in. As in, "Wait a minute, what if I need this thing after all?" It's OK to feel that way, and you might at first.

But the yardstick to measure whether it stays or goes should be this: *if it isn't serving you right now, let it go.* If you haven't worn it for six months or longer, you probably won't anytime soon. So, move it. Clear it out. Find it a new home.

That means giving it away. Donating it, giving it to a friend or family member, or even selling it. After all, just because something has served its purpose for you doesn't mean it can't be of service for someone else. That's the beauty of decluttering your space. Not only do you free up energy in your life for new things to come in, but you give what you let go of a chance to bring joy to someone else.

Whether you believe it or not, there is someone out there who would love your worn-out flip flops, your old black dress, or your worn-out jacket. But when you hold onto it for whatever reason – be it guilt, fear, or lack mentality – it doesn't serve anybody. Then again, if you share it, if you put it back into the Universe and give someone else the chance to enjoy it, it can serve a whole new purpose. You might be convinced that nobody would have any interest in your raggedy old sweater or your old winter coat. But trust me, there is someone out there who is looking for the very thing that is cluttering your space right now. When you release something with love, you give that item an opportunity to receive new energy – and bring new energy to another person. What better way to help an old thing become new again?

One more thing to remember, too: I'm not telling you to get rid of your stuff because you don't deserve it. It's not because I believe that it's not 'spiritual' to have possessions that you love. What I'm talking about is releasing things that keep you stuck in old, outdated patterns. It's about letting things go that are holding you back. We want to move the old energy out to make space for the new.

What happens next? With all of the space you create, maybe give yourself the opportunity to replace it with something new. Something that represents who you are NOW. It could be new clothes, new decorations, new books. It doesn't matter. If you feel called to it, bring in something that feels good to you, something that honors the person you are TODAY rather than the person you were yesterday.

So today, you're going to declutter two areas. First, your physical space. The things you hold onto in the physical world. And we're going to focus specifically on the closet. Second, we're going to clear out your mental space. We're going to bring up thoughts that take up excess space in your mental container. You're going to look at them, affirm something different, and release them.

Today is all about clearing space, both inside and out.

What's the Bottom Line?

- Clutter shows up in your physical space *and* your mental space

- What shows up on the outside reflects what is happening on the inside

- Let go of what no longer serves you and create space for new energy

Practical Action Steps for Today...

Start with your mental space today. Notice your thoughts and identify three to five old ideas that take up space and give you nothing in return. Bring them up, write them down, and look at them without judgment. Then, for each cluttered thought, affirm the opposite. Throughout the day, when one of the old ideas rears its head, thank it for sharing. Tell it you're not interested. Then tell it you're going to focus on something else now.

Next, let's tackle the closet! Today you're going to choose three to five things that you're ready to part with. It could be anything that doesn't serve you anymore. Clothes that don't fit, shoes that aren't your style, things that represent a bygone time. From there, you can donate them, give them away, or even sell them. The goal is the get them out of your closet and back into the world again.

Today's goal is to at least get them out of the closet. Take it away. Don't just hold onto it. If getting it out of your home is too much for right now, at the very least, move it outside of your closet. Even if it's just to your garage or your attic.

As you're doing this, pay attention to how it feels. Why did you choose the items that you did? How did it feel to move it up and out of your space?

Let's Write This! Questions to Ponder...

Part 1: Decluttering your mind

Pay attention to your thoughts today. What goes through your mind on a daily basis, and do these ideas serve you? What are the thoughts that keep you stuck in negative patterns? Are you ready and willing to let them go? Write them down below.

_____
_____
_____
_____
_____
_____
_____
_____
_____
_____

Now, appreciate the old thoughts for sharing, and tell them you're not interested.
"Thank you for sharing, but I'm not interested."
For each negative thought, turn it on its head and affirm the opposite. Write down the new version of each old idea right here.

_____
_____
_____
_____
_____
_____
_____
_____
_____
_____

Now, put it all together! For each time the cluttered thought shows up ...

Thanks for sharing ...
I'm not interested.
I'm choosing to focus on ...
Affirm the opposite.

That's it! Repeat this process as often as you need to throughout the day.

Part 2: Decluttering your space

Step into your closet and take a good look around. Get a feel for the energy and see what calls to your attention. What are the items that cause you stress, anxiety, or pain? What three to five items are you letting go of today? Write them down below.

_____

_____

_____

_____

_____

_____

_____

_____

_____

Why have these things taken up space for so long? For each item that has run its course, ask yourself why it has outstayed its welcome. What does it represent to you? Why did it stay in your closet as long as it did? Make a few notes about each thing below.

_____

_____

_____

_____

_____
_____
_____
_____
_____
_____

How did it feel to let it go? What feelings came up as you parted ways with each item? It might be relief, excitement, maybe even fear or anxiety. Pay attention to your feelings and write down what came up for you in the space below.

_____
_____
_____
_____
_____
_____
_____
_____
_____
_____
_____

Part 3: What are you inviting in? (Optional)

What are you bringing into your space? It's entirely optional, but if you feel called to replace the old with the new, go for it! If you choose to welcome new items into your space, make sure that you're bringing in something that represents who you are NOW. Something that lifts your Spirit and makes you feel good.

What are those items for you? Make a few notes about each thing and what it represents for you.

_____
_____
_____
_____

_____

_____

_____

_____

_____

_____

_____

_____

_____

_____

_____

DAY 18: AGREEMENTS, CONTRACTS, AND VOWS: ARE THEY SERVING YOU ANYMORE?

We've all made promises, agreements, and pacts in life. Sometimes we're aware of them. Other times, we're not. But you make them all the time, with yourself and others.

What do I mean by agreements? I mean arrangements that you create for yourself and with other people to ensure specific outcomes. We're talking about things that you swear by, that you'll either "always" or "never" do, usually based on an experience that went very well ... or very poorly.

Of course, an agreement that you made might've seemed like a good idea at the time. Perhaps it was the only logical or reasonable response to the situation you were in at that moment. But too many times, old promises become lifetime warranties, whether they're still working after all these years or not.

If you're like everyone else, you've probably noticed that you have patterns. Things that you've always done, whether you were aware of it or not. But maybe those unconscious choices that you've made over the years have stemmed from a contract that you made. A promise, a vow to keep something precisely as it is.

And it's possible that some of those deals might've outlasted their usefulness.

Today we're going to talk about agreements. Contracts that you've made with yourself and others, for whatever reason. And I'm going to show you why some contracts can be renegotiated, or even broken.

Maybe you took a vow of silence that you weren't aware of that caused you not to speak up, regardless of what kinds of abuse or injustices you might've witnessed. It could be that you took a vow of poverty, and it's been preventing you from receiving the abundance that you crave. Maybe you believe that your body isn't a safe place to live in, and you've put up walls of protection (such as holding onto weight). You might've agreed not to be seen because for some reason you believe that getting attention is not safe.

You might not have a clue how or why you made a particular contract, or even that such an arrangement exists. But I bet you know what I mean when I say it.

Sometimes contracts and agreements can't be boiled down to simple ideas like silence, poverty, or protection. But no matter how complicated or simple they are, the more you explore this, the more you will see that those agreements are there. And they might be manifesting in a way that doesn't serve your purpose the way that they once did.

But whatever agreements were made, regardless of when you made them, at what age you made them, or in whatever lifetime you made them, if you bring awareness to them, you can heal them.

In some cases, all you have to do is ask to receive the awareness you need. And if the memory arises, you have the power to infuse it with light and healing. If you allow yourself to feel the pain, bring it up and move it out, you can free it from your body.

Maybe the seed of an agreement was planted years, decades, or even lifetimes ago. Maybe it wasn't a conscious choice at the time. Perhaps it made sense when it was first planted. But now, you are a new person who has the ability and the responsibility to choose differently.

After all, something in you probably wants to create new experiences, or you would not be here with me right now. That's how I know that you're ready for something new. So, let's get that started right now.

Not too long ago, I was working with a client at a workshop called *"Embracing Your Body."* Just like many of us, this particular client told me that she has had a long-standing struggle losing weight. I asked her if she knew when this battle began, but she couldn't give me an answer. Of course, I knew that she knew on some level. It was just up to us to go within and see what we could discover.

I walked her through a visualization technique that took her back through her history. The key was to find where the desire for protection came from. For many of us, holding on to extra weight is about keeping additional security, and I had a feeling this was the case with this client. We intended to discover where the need for the extra protection was coming from.

As we started the journey inward, though, I started getting different insights. What we discovered was that the weight wasn't necessarily about protection. It was an agreement that she'd made with herself. So, we shifted our focus to looking for the contract that was made long ago. And what happened next was fascinating.

She grew up on the East Coast In a lower middle-class neighborhood, a place where the streets were a little bit tougher than average. Her family didn't have a lot of extra money, so treats were rare at her house.

In the summertime when the ice cream truck came through the neighborhood, all the kids would come running. She would always beg her parents for change, but they rarely had anything to give her. She'd only be treated to ice cream once a month, if at all. It was a treat when they said yes, but it was a rare treat. Most of the time she'd run out to the ice cream truck only to be disappointed. She'd see all the other neighborhood kids getting ice cream, and it made her feel left out.

We uncovered a specific memory somewhere around age nine. She started running out the ice cream truck one day, but her parents told her, "We don't have money for that." With her hands on her hips, she said, "When I grow up, nobody is ever going to tell me that I can't have ice cream. I'm going to have whatever I want. And I'm gonna buy it for myself."

And surprise, surprise: what do you think one of her most significant emotional comfort foods was up until then? Ice cream.

She had agreed that nobody was going to control her food choices. Nobody would ever tell her that she couldn't have what she wanted. So even when she tried every diet out there and worked with all the weight loss experts she could find, nothing ever worked. Subconsciously, she was rebelling against everyone who told her what she could not have. And it all went back to being denied a treat from the ice cream truck.

As an adult, she never even told herself no, especially when it came to food. Sure, after she ate it, she'd punish herself. But if she wanted it, she'd have it. Nobody would ever tell her NO.

Over the years, that deep agreement became a pattern. And now it was a pattern that was causing her a lot of pain.

With that insight and awareness, things shifted for her. She realized that it was an agreement that was made a long time ago. Maybe it made sense at the time. But it was not serving her anymore. And it was time to renegotiate the contract.

I can't say that I know of such a specific agreement in my own life, which is why I share her remarkable story with you. But in my experience, I do remember lessons of comparison and judgment. Telling myself what I could and couldn't have. Those things are contracts and agreements, too. And you can let them go at any time.

Everyone has the power to renegotiate an agreement, whether it is with yourself or someone else. Just because it made sense decades ago doesn't mean that it serves the person who you are today. That is the bottom line.

You might believe that you're locked into all the agreements that you made in this life. But the truth is that as a Spirit in a human body, you can change your mind. No contract is final. We all make agreements, many of which are made unconsciously. Others not. But either way, they can be changed, renegotiated, or broken at any time. That goes for contracts that you made with yourself and even agreements with others. If a deal involves another person, for example, you can't change other people's choices, opinions, or actions. But you can choose to see agreements another way. And you can renegotiate them within yourself, if nowhere else.

That's what we're focusing on today. We all have contracts and agreements that might have outlived their usefulness. But first, you need to know what they are. You also need to have the willingness to release them.

Now, do you have to know the complete terms and details of an agreement to let it go? Not necessarily. Sometimes setting the intention to release the constrictive energy of an old contract is enough. Saying that you desire to let go of something that needs to be released is often sufficient. You don't have to know exactly what it is to let it go. (This is especially true in cases such as sexual abuse, where people sometimes have behaviors and responses, but might not have full access to the triggering memory.)

Your Mind, Body, and Spirit are always helping you heal if you're willing to allow it. And a lot of the time, your conscious mind doesn't have to experience the memory of something to improve it. You can release something without going deeply into it. Setting the intention to dismiss anything that no longer serves you for your highest and greatest good is a perfect place to start.

So today, I want you to know that you can renegotiate your agreements. You can get married; you can get divorced. In a relationship, you can agree to cook dinner every night, then decide ten years down the road that it's time for a change in routine. Others can choose to agree with your new terms, or not. But you can make choices for yourself at any time.

People play roles in your life, and you play roles in their lives as well. The key is to recognize the value in the experiences we have with ourselves and with others. I'm not saying this is easy. Sometimes letting go of old ideas can get ugly and nasty. There might be a lot of resistance. And that is OK. The thing is, you can hold onto whatever you choose to, and for as long as you wish. No judgment. All I'm saying is that when you allow yourself to move through your resistance, bring up the pain that you've been pushing down, and release it, there is freedom on the other side.

There is no right or wrong in your choices. I just want to remind you that you can choose.

Now, you might be wondering how you can tell if an agreement, a contract, or a vow has been made in the first place. How do you identify them so that they can be released? One sign is holding on to physical weight. Or, they also might show up as an overwhelming fear that doesn't make any sense. Health conditions or illnesses might be another clue ... possibly conflicts with other people that make you feel stuck. It could also translate as a struggle with money. Any or all of these signs might point to an agreement or a vow that was made, consciously or not.

We're talking about recurring patterns that manifest in lower vibrational ways. They can be restrictive, they can feed your fears, and they can hold you back from the life that you want to live.

Whatever agreements that you've made, they have served you in the past. But just because they were right at one moment doesn't mean that they have no expiration date. If an old contract's time is up, renegotiate it. Adjust it. You don't need anybody else's permission or approval. Change it to something that serves the person you are today.

Now, with any change, there might be sadness. You're letting go of an identity you've connected to for a long time. Whether it was an identity that supported you or not, it's still a known commodity. Sometimes even painful things can be familiar and comfortable. There can be a sense of grief or loss in this process. You might also find several layers of emotion that need to be peeled back, one at a time. That's OK, too. The more of that energy that you can bring up and out, the closer you'll be to freedom. Freedom from feeling stuck and disconnected. Freedom from old agreements, vows, and contracts running your life.

Freedom is on the other side.

As you explore all of this, pay close attention to the insights you receive. Where did your arrangements begin? How have you supported these agreements through your beliefs and actions? Are these agreements necessary anymore? And do you want to take your power back from that situation, person, or experience today? The good news is that you CAN.

What's the Bottom Line?

- Agreements, contracts, and vows can be made at any time

- They can be made with or without your conscious awareness

- When agreements were made, they served you in some way

- They might not be serving you anymore, however

- You can renegotiate or let go of an agreement at any time

Practical Action Steps for Today...

In the place that you are today, right now, in this lifetime, I'm going to share a few questions with you. Questions that I hope will bring you insight, awareness, and a willingness to let go of these agreements ... to clear out space for new energy and life. It's time to start opening up and becoming aware.

Ask yourself these questions, then just listen.

Are there any agreements that I have made, consciously or not, that no longer serve me?

What are the patterns of this agreement? How does this contract show up in my life, and how can I begin to recognize it?

What am I gaining from this agreement? How has this agreement served me in the past?

What can I learn from this agreement?

Am I ready to release this agreement for my highest good?

As you ask these questions, what do you become aware of? Maybe you feel lighter. Perhaps asking causes your heartbeat to race. You might feel sad, frustrated, or angry. That's OK. It just means that you've found another layer, and you're getting closer to freedom. Repeat this process as many times as you need to. It wasn't intended to be a one-and-done sort of thing.

Make sure as you go along that you are writing the energy and the emotion out of you. Feeling the pain is OK, but I don't want you to get stuck there. Get it out of your body and onto paper. Burn it if you feel the need. It's time to transmute and release that energy. And it might take more than once.

Ask yourself each question, open up for guidance, and just listen. Allow the answers to flow to you and through you, then write it all down below or in your journal.

Don't worry if you don't get crystal-clear specific answers. Go with what you know at the moment. Remember that this might take more than one try. Come back to these questions as often as you need to.

Question 1: Are there any agreements that I made, consciously or not, that no longer serve me?

_____
_____
_____
_____
_____
_____
_____
_____
_____
_____

Question 2: What are the patterns of this agreement? How has it been showing up in my life, and how can I recognize it?

_____
_____
_____
_____
_____
_____
_____
_____
_____

Question 3: What am I gaining from keeping this agreement? How has it served me up until now?

_____
_____
_____
_____
_____
_____
_____
_____
_____
_____

Question 4: What can I learn from this agreement?

_____
_____
_____
_____
_____
_____
_____
_____
_____
_____
_____

Question 5: Am I ready to release this agreement for my highest and greatest good? _Am I ready?_

_____
_____
_____
_____
_____
_____

BODY REVIVAL WORKBOOK

_____

_____

_____

_____

Question 6: How does it feel to let go of this agreement?

_____

_____

_____

_____

_____

_____

_____

_____

_____

Write down what comes up for you. Allow any pain or fear to flow through you and onto the paper. Feel free to burn these sheets if you're called to do so. The key is to release as much as you are ready and willing to release.

DAY 19: BEAUTY SLEEP –
HEALING YOUR BFF THROUGH REST

Most of the topics throughout this 22-day experience are areas that have challenged me in the past. Every single one of them I've gone through myself. I've learned what I needed to learn. I've moved my way through them, I've found the way out, and now I'm sharing those experiences with you.

This topic, though, is something that I'm still learning as I go. I still struggle with it; I'm not going to lie. Sometimes I follow through better than others. But although it's a work in progress in my life, I have gotten a lot closer to embracing it with more consistency. And as I've said from day one, we're not shooting for perfection here. Just progress. And consistency is the way to get there.

The topic is Rest and Sleep. Taking enough time to rest your body and getting enough sleep to renew your body. Now, I can't tell you all the specific techniques to master this one. Like I mentioned, I'm still learning myself. But over the past year or so, I can tell you that I've made significant strides. I've learned more about the necessity of sleep. I've become more able to take a few steps away from the computer and the office from time to time and let myself rest. And I'm going to share with you the tips and tricks that have gotten me this far and are helping me continue the journey.

I did a little bit of research and came up with some numbers of interest for you. About 40% of Americans are sleep-deprived. What constitutes "sleep deprivation?" Less than seven hours per night. And roughly ⅔ of Americans don't get enough "catch up" sleep on the weekends. What's more, when you're deprived of adequate rest, your stress levels skyrocket, your cortisol levels shoot up, and your brain and body can't help but react. And I fully believe that over time, this is a significant factor in manifesting disease.

Stress and anxiety can show up if you're having trouble falling asleep, too. Think about it for a moment. What happens when you're struggling to fall asleep, but it just isn't happening? Where does your mind go? Unfortunately, it doesn't usually focus on all the beautiful things in your life. It often lands on all the things you've been worrying about all day. Money. Relationships. Life. And it usually doesn't shut up, does it? Of course, your body reacts to that, too.

Another consequence of sleep deprivation is that it tends to have the same effect as a few drinks. If you haven't had enough sleep over an extended enough period, it can be tantamount to showing up drunk. So that can translate into driving drunk. Working drunk. Teaching drunk.

Now do I believe that every single person needs seven hours of sleep every single night? Probably not. It's merely a guideline. But no matter who you are, at some point you need to refuel. That's what I came to realize myself, and that's why I decided to make it a priority.

For many years, I thought that getting enough sleep wasn't a big deal for me. I was sure I could get by on 5 to 5 ½ hours a night. Six hours was like sleeping in for me. I was feeling good, not getting sick, and getting crazy amounts of work done. And I figured that if it ain't broke, don't fix it.

Now, I've been studying and training with Brendon Burchard for about three years. One thing that he has you do is look at all the areas of your life and give yourself a little assessment. Things like moving your body, increasing your productivity, creating time and energy for yourself and your projects. I had that all down, no problems there. But another area he always addressed was sleep. And it was the one that I chose to blow off. I figured I was doing just fine in that area, and that the sleep assessments didn't apply to me.

Of course, sometimes denial means resistance. Finally, I leveled with myself. I didn't believe that the sleep factor "applied to me" because I just found it uncomfortable. Not that I knew why just yet. But there was definitely resistance.

Eventually, I decided to take the sleep thing a little bit more seriously and learn not only why sleep was so crucial to well-being, but also why I felt such resistance to getting more of it for myself.

When I finally decided to get this "slumber party" started, my goal was to get at least 6 hours of sleep every night. You might've heard me say before that I'm an early riser. I get up at about 4:30 every morning. As far as going to bed at night, that time usually turned into whenever I finished with work (which means anything from 10 PM to the wee hours of the morning).

Now, as I mentioned, science says that we need at least 7 hours a night. And with all that I have going on, it was more than safe to say that I wasn't getting anywhere near that amount. Seven hours seemed too much of a stretch for me. But I thought that six hours might be an achievable happy medium, so I made that the goal.

That took care of the "sleep" part of the plan. The "rest" part, though? That was another story. I was never very good at taking naps. The only time I ever took an actual nap was when my body threatened me with collapse. And as far as making time to just BE, without DOING something? Hardly my strong suit.

So, what was my real resistance to rest, and where did that struggle come from? The more that I focused on getting more sleep, the more that the real reason for the resistance started to reveal itself.

When I was growing up, my parents were both very active. Both of them were perfectionists in their own way. My mother always had the house looking perfectly tidy and beautiful, with everything in its place. Now, she put most of the pressure for the perfect home on herself. Us kids did have some household chores, but she didn't make us a part of her need for domestic perfection. It wasn't so much her as it was my dad.

Most of the time my dad was working, so he wasn't around the house that much. But when he was home, he expected things to look and be a particular way. Including all of us.

I remember a specific instance when I was nine years old. I was laying on the floor in the living room listening to a Carole King album, dreamily enjoying the music.

Then my dad came into the room and asked me what I was doing. I said I was listening to the song. He then said, "You have to do something. Just go DO something."

Well, that sort of thing happened often. If we were sitting and doing something that seemed like nothing, doing something that he didn't consider worthwhile, then we weren't doing anything. So, when he was around, we all had to look at least like we were doing something. No reading, no playing, no listening to music. Something that he would consider constructive.

How did I respond? I got smart. I kept a bottle of Windex and a roll of paper towels underneath my bed. When I heard my dad come home, I would grab them, go into the bathroom right around the corner, and start cleaning something. Surely that passed for "doing something."

So, if my dad was around, we had to be doing something. And if we weren't, he'd give us something to do. Simple as that.

What was the message there? The message was that there was no value in sitting, resting, or just being. If you weren't actively engaged, you were wasting your time. That's what I learned. That's what I integrated. And what I internalized was that you don't have value if you weren't continually DOING.

Somehow, I bet you can relate to this one way or another.

That was the first revelation. The second thing I realized was that one of my other challenges in life has always been feeling pressed for time. I've always felt rushed, like I would never have enough time for all the things I've wanted to do. Now, I have a full life, which I love. I'm a very active person, which I also love. There are so many things that are hugely important to me. Sometimes it all feels like too much of a good thing, though, because the struggle always becomes, "How will I have time for all of this?"

I wake up in the morning, and I'm excited. I want to create this program, and I want to get that book done. I want to spend time with my children, take my granddaughters to the movies, and travel with my husband. I want to hang out with my team and see my friends. So many things that I want to do. But I've never felt as though I had enough time for it all.

So as much as I've come to appreciate that I am a human BEING, not a human DOING, rest and sleep is still a challenge for me. But there have been significant improvements in the last few months and years, too. For instance, I can take a few minutes to sit down even if the room isn't spotless. Leaving the dishes in the sink overnight once in a while doesn't make me break out in hives. Slowly but surely, I'm letting go of the pressure I've always put on myself to be in a constant state of GO.

That was my challenge. Now I'm going to share some of the things I learned around it.

First and foremost, sleep allows you to heal. When you sleep, you take the pressure off of your brain, your body, and even your cells. Natural healing occurs during sleep. Don't wait for your body to let you know by breaking down that you need rest. Because if you do wait until then, the breakdown will happen. (Interestingly enough, nearly every disease there is has at least one aspect of it that is tied to inadequate sleep.)

It makes sense if you consider it. When kids aren't feeling well, for example, what do we tell them to do? Lie down, get some rest, take a nap. And most of the time, a good sleep does the trick, doesn't it? Sleep allows your body to heal. If it doesn't have the necessary healing time, that's when illnesses and diseases can either creep in. Or get worse.

So today, the focus is taking the time to rest. Maybe for you, that is taking a nap. (The ideal amount of time for a "power nap," according to the experts, is 20 minutes, by the way.) Or maybe just laying your body down somewhere and just resting. Just being present. Perhaps it's taking some time to read, paint your fingernails, or listen to music. Or just walking away from the environment you're in for a short time. Give yourself a chance to recalibrate your energy by stepping back from doing, and just being.

That takes care of rest. Now, let's talk about sleep. How many hours do you usually get every day? Is falling asleep easy for you? Maybe you aren't getting nearly enough rest. But then again, perhaps you're getting too much, too. Sometimes too much sleep can be a wake-up call just as much as too little sleep, as it might indicate a little bit of depression going on.

What I suggest is creating a routine especially for sleep. Many of us have habits in the evening (whether they're formal or not). You eat dinner, and you watch TV, you go to bed. Why not create some space to improve your chances of a good night's sleep?

Here's what I would suggest ...

First of all, no screens one hour before bedtime. That means no phones, no computers, no iPads, no television. I know, that sounds impossible. (Especially the no phone part, right?) But I promise, there's a reason why I'm suggesting something that seems so restrictive. Research has shown that with any screen, it emits a kind of light that activates your brain. So, if you are playing round after round of Candy Crush or binge-watching Netflix right before you switch off the light, you probably won't drift right off to sleep. What's more is that when your brain is stimulated in this way, you're a lot less likely to get the deep, quality, REM sleep that your body craves.

Turn off the electronics one hour before you hit the hay. Feel free to read a book, write in your journal, or listen to music. But let the technology rest right along with you.

Try a bath or a shower just before bedtime. We've talked about the healing power of water, and this is another way that you can harness that power. Not only does the water calm your energy, but you can also consider it a beautiful stream that washes away the energetic debris of the day. Try visualizing the water washing away the things that no longer serve you, both physical and spiritual.

Another thing you can include is what I call a brain dump. This means simply writing down everything that is in your head. It's getting out all of the stress, anxiety, and stinkin' thinkin' that tends to run through your mind the harder you try to fall asleep. You know, the things that people say "keep them awake at night?" More often that means fears, frustrations, and everything that isn't working in their lives. If you fall asleep with that kind of mental shit show going on, your quality of sleep will be nowhere near adequate.

If you can't fall asleep because your mind starts racing the moment your head hits the pillow, this might just be a fit for you. Grab a pen and paper, write it all down, and get it out of your head and onto the page. When you're finished, take a deep breath, find your center again, and shift your vibration to appreciation. After you take out the mental trash, fill up that space by jotting down five to ten things you're grateful for. Take that vibration to sleep with you instead of the mental strife and watch what happens.

Along the lines of appreciation, meditation or prayer is the perfect ending to a bedtime routine. Maybe a short meditation, a visualization, Reiki, or energy healing work calls to you. No matter what you choose, allow it to move you into a calm and gentle space before you go to sleep.

Now, of course, the second part of the sleep pattern is waking up. That means making the morning routine a priority as well. Once again, that means eliminate the screens. Avoid your iPad, smartphone, or television for an hour after you get up. I know, that also sounds like too much of a challenge. But there's a reason for it, too. Most of us start our day in a reactive mode. We turn on the TV, look at our phones, and get onto social media. Then we start reacting to emails, text messages, and Facebook feeds (to say nothing of the stories on the morning news). Wouldn't it be great to set an intention to create your day, rather than have it designed for you? Wouldn't it be amazing to decide what you want to experience, rather than react to what is being hurled at you by TV, phones, and social media?

Sounds a lot better to me, too.

Today's focus is sleep and rest. I know it might be a challenging one. But sleep is absolutely necessary to serve your BFF. Give her the rest, relaxation, and sleep she needs. Even if you're like me and it's a work in progress. Progress is the important thing here.

What's the Bottom Line?

- Nearly half of all Americans don't get enough sleep

- Lack of sleep is linked to many diseases

- Sleep routines will ensure adequate and higher quality sleep

- Don't skip out on sleep. Your BFF needs it.

Practical Action Steps for Today...

Today I want you to pay attention to your sleep patterns and habits. How much sleep are you getting every night? How long does it take for you to fall asleep? What is your goal? Where could you put forth a little bit of extra effort, and what are you willing to do to ensure that this plan goes well for you?

Then I'd like you to create a new sleep routine. Give yourself at least seven hours of sleep and create the space to make that fit into your life.

As you create this routine, pay attention to what side of the sleep fence that you fall on right now. Many of us don't get enough sleep. But then again, some of us use rest as an escape. If you find that sometimes you go to bed to have a place to hide, that might be worth exploring too. Make a note of where you are and create a plan for where you'd like to go.

Remember, the guidelines are seven to nine hours a night. Integrate this into your life in a way that works for you.

It might not work perfectly on the first try. But give it a chance at least for today. Give yourself the opportunity to have a new experience and see how it works out for you.

Let's Write This! Questions to Ponder...

Part 1: Create your sleep routine. How will you create and implement your new routine? Keeping all of the above in mind, answer the following questions.

My goal is_____ hours of sleep each night.

I usually require _____ (minutes) to fall asleep each night.

I plan to wake up at _____ (time).

Therefore, bedtime will be at _____ (time).

Part 2: Working rest into your day. How will you include resting time for your Mind, Body, and Spirit? It could be a nap. Maybe a short walk. It could be a reading break or music break. Perhaps a few brief moments to sit quietly and DO nothing.

Write down two to three options for rest that appeal to you, and work at least one of them into your day today.

_____
_____
_____
_____
_____
_____
_____
_____
_____
_____
_____

Part 3: The results of your "sleep study." How did your new rest and sleep routine work for you? What worked, what didn't? Make a few notes below.

_____
_____
_____
_____
_____
_____
_____
_____
_____
_____
_____

How did it feel to incorporate rest into your day? Did you notice a change in your energy or productivity? Maybe some unexpected result? Write down your impressions here.

_____
_____
_____
_____
_____
_____
_____
_____
_____
_____
_____

How did the sleep routine work for you? Were you able to get the amount of sleep you desired? How did the "screen break" affect your quality of sleep? Did you notice a difference?

What worked for you and what didn't? Write down your impressions as well as any adjustments you'd like to make.

_____
_____
_____
_____
_____
_____
_____
_____
_____
_____
_____

DAY 20: A "TOUCHY" SUBJECT (THE IMPORTANCE OF PHYSICAL CONNECTION)

Today I'm taking on a topic that I don't think I've ever explicitly covered before. It has been a part of other workshops, books, or programs, but not quite to this degree of devotion. But it's a super-important one, albeit a little on the sensitive side. Let's get into a new day with a subject that is both basic and profound.

This topic might be comfortable for some of us and daunting for others. But no matter how you feel about it, it's something that you need in your life. That something is TOUCH.

I mean a physical connection with yourself and with others. We're talking physical connections. And they come in many forms. It could be hugging, kissing, or pats on the back. Maybe it's massage, handshakes, or even masturbation. Physical bodies need a physical connection. And honestly, many of us are starving for this kind of contact, no matter what our life situation might be.

Now, not every single version of touch applies to every person. But every person requires some form of it. Whether you know it or not, in these physical containers, human contact is essential. "Real-world" physical touch.

Now, touch can be a delicate topic. There are many of us with specific challenges in this area, and I want to acknowledge that. I mean things like previous experiences of pain, trauma, or abuse. Some of us have experienced physical or sexual abuse that translated as uninvited touch. Others were raised with belief systems that have made contact a sensitive (if not an off-limits) subject.

There is also the potential for judgment and criticism in the desire for touch. Maybe even rejection. Like a moment when you open your arms to hug somebody, and they don't embrace you back. Or when you reach out with a sexual invitation and your partner doesn't respond. Perhaps you try to express your love through a kiss, and the other person turns away. We're talking about the possibility of being shut down. That's some pretty big-time vulnerability, isn't it?

But regardless of your background or your viewpoints about it, physical connection in some form is necessary for life. After all, babies need it even to survive. And every human being needs it to thrive.

Now, I'm not saying I'm an expert in this field. But I do fully embrace the power of touch. If you've been to any of my in-person workshops, you'll get a big hug from me (as I'm not much of a handshake kind of gal). I'm a pretty touchy-feely person, and with good reason. Touch is powerful, and it's something I feel is important to share. I want to empower you with the gift of touch, too.

Let's get a specific example here. What does a hug do for you? Here are just a few of the benefits of a good ol' fashioned embrace ...

- More upbeat moods
- Reduced heart rates
- Reduced blood pressure
- Increased nerve activity
- Reduced cortisol levels, which is your stress hormone
- Increased levels of oxytocin, which is your bonding hormone
- Boost in the immune system
- Increased self-esteem
- Alleviated tension
- Production of endorphins

AND...

- It doesn't cost a thing

Cuddling or hugging another person boosts your feelings of self-worth, belonging, and appreciation. It encourages bonding by increasing levels of the hormone oxytocin, which makes you feel more safe, secure, and loved. Hugs decrease feelings of loneliness, they combat fear, and they affirm relationships.

Studies have shown that IQ development is delayed in children who don't receive regular hugs. According to an American survey, marriages that include more hugging and touching last longer than those that don't. People crave at least 13 hugs a day, but most of us don't receive nearly that many.

Then, how about the benefits of even more intimate encounters? Healthy, consensual sex (however you define it) lowers blood pressure, boosts libido, and increases bladder control in women. It lowers heart attack risk, lessens pain, and improves sleep. And of course, it creates trust and connection between partners.

There are a lot of reasons to hug, have sex, or anything in between. It all qualifies as physical touch.

The struggle ensues, though, because so many of us have stories about physical touch. It might have been an experience where contact was unsafe or unwanted. Some of us have had moments where they were taken advantage of or have even taken advantage of others. There might've been rejection or pain that went along with the experience, too. I'm not an expert, but I do recognize that there are a lot of pieces to this puzzle.

Today's topic might be a daunting one, and I understand that. But here's all that I am asking you today: I'm asking you to see that as an energetic being in a physical body, you *can* call in what you need. You have choices. You can choose what you will allow your body to experience. If you're ready, you can receive the positive aspects of touch at any time. I encourage you to get out there today, get a hug, make some human connection, and feel the life-affirming beauty of touch for yourself.

How can you kindly and lovingly create experiences of touch? Let's talk about some of the ways that you can connect with yourself and others. My favorite way (much to my husband's chagrin) is hugs. I'm a hugger, and I'm a toucher. I love that this is an easy and accessible way to connect with people. Of course, sometimes you need to ask because you don't want to take advantage of the other person's space. But when you get the green light, hugs are one of the easiest ways to connect with your fellow human beings.

Several years ago, a friend of mine named Carol Miller invited me to participate in "International Hug Day." Now, that sounded right up my alley, so naturally I jumped at the chance. So, we grabbed our "free hugs" signs, went out to Westgate here in Glendale, Arizona, and set up shop. And let me tell you, the results of our efforts were fascinating.

Some people jumped at the chance and were like, "Yeah! Free hugs!" Others here hesitant at first, but eventually eased in and joined the party. Then there were some who gave us the cold shoulder and turned away altogether. Of course, there was no right or wrong in any of their responses, and I didn't judge a single person. But it was curious to note different people's reactions and responses to an invitation of touch.

We've made "Hug Day" a regular thing ever since, even if on a smaller scale. This past year, we held our hug-a-thon party on a cruise, and it was a fabulous experience. I noticed that the cruise created a built-in sense of community, and people were even more agreeable to bonding experiences, even with strangers.

Of course, when we're in our usual environments and situations, opening up and trusting isn't always as easy. But it can be done with a little bit of intention and practice.

Touch is vital in everybody's life. We talked about how babies need it to survive. But studies have also shown that elders over the age of 80 need touch to the same degree as infants. I saw that for myself during the years I spent as a hospice volunteer.

Then again, those of us who live alone might encounter the same issue. If you live by yourself, you might have limitations on the amount of touch you receive. Even if you do live around children, grandchildren, or spouses, the home environment you experienced growing up might affect your capacity to receive touch. There are a lot of pieces at work here.

But like anything else, if you desire change, you can create it. You can create a space where you can give and receive touch safely and lovingly. It might take some deeper self-exploration, but you can make it happen.

Honestly, I think that human connection is something that a lot of us want but very few of us know how to ask for. Sometimes a hug is all it would take to resolve an argument, but most of us are afraid to open up for fear of rejection. But the truth is this: you can't experience the gratitude of the moment without having some vulnerability. You can't go from "I want this" to "I have this" without taking a chance and opening up. That's where the trust comes in.

Healing touch, physical touch, and supporting ourselves with human contact – that is the focus for today. I want you to focus on where your history has been in regard to touch. If you find that you're stuck in old patterns that deny you the experience you want, take action today. If there are areas that you tend to resist, step into that. If you believe that you don't give enough hugs to others, reach out to somebody and make an offer for a loving embrace. If you need a hug yourself, ask for one. If you've been missing a strong sexual connection in your relationship, maybe it's time to bring some intimacy back to the picture. They key is to look at your past, see where you might be holding back, and determine what you wish to change. Then decide what change looks like for you and take at least one step forward.

If you've ever seen the movie "*Saved by The Light,*" it portrays the value of touch and connection in a beautiful way. It's the story of a man named Dannion Brinkley, a man who spent his life bullying other people. His story is that he was struck by lightning and had a near-death experience. During the time of that experience, he learned that there was an energetic and emotional connection with everyone he met. He also learned that any pain that he projected onto others would eventually come back to him during his life review. When he came back, he made a promise to take every opportunity to hug, squeeze, and love every person that he met. Why? Because knew that in the end, he'd receive it all back.

He laughingly said that this choice was a selfish one. I believe it's a beautiful one. If you share a lot of love here on earth and you get it back when you leave, well, why not start sharing the love right now?

That's the beauty of human connection right there. It has the potential to bring more peace and joy into your life and create those same feelings for others. What could be better?

But it all starts with YOU.

What's the Bottom Line?

- In our physical bodies, touch is a vital part of the experience

- Too many of us don't get the physical connection that we crave

- Touch can be anything, from handshakes to hugs to sex

- Touch can be a sensitive issue for many of us, but that can be changed

Practical Action Steps for Today...

Today, start by asking yourself how touch makes you feel. How often do you touch another person? How often does someone touch you? Would you like to have more touch in your life?
Consider these questions and do a bit of journaling around your answers. Have you ever been resistant to touch, and if so, what are the reasons behind that?

Second, if touch is what you wish for, reach out and ask for what you want! Maybe it's an extra hug. Perhaps a handshake instead of a simple wave. It might even be scheduling a long-overdue massage. But the key is to see where you are, decide where you want to go, and from there take action to get closer to what you truly want.

Let's Write This! Questions to Ponder...

Part 1: How much touch do you have in your life? Take a look at the questions below and consider your current life as well as your history.

What does the idea of "touch" bring up for you? Make a few notes on what surfaces for you here.

_____

_____

_____

_____

_____

How often do you touch other people on a daily basis, and how often to others touch you? It doesn't have to be exact numbers, just a ballpark idea. Write it down here.

_____

_____

_____

_____

_____

Do you feel that this amount of interaction is adequate? Why or why not?

_____

_____

_____

_____

_____

Have you ever been resistant to touch? If so, what do you believe are the reasons behind that? Make a few notes about what comes up for you.

_____

_____

_____

_____
_____
_____

Part 2: Bringing more touch to your life (if desired!) Are you craving more physical connection with people, however it might show up? Let's look into that here.

_____
_____
_____
_____
_____

What kinds of connections are you desiring? Is it more hugs or cuddles? Maybe a closer sexual relationship with your partner? Or just a simple pat on the back now and then? Write down what you want to experience. And as you go along, acknowledge the feelings that come up as well.

_____
_____
_____
_____
_____

Ask for what you want. Whatever kind of closeness you desire, take a little bit of action towards it today. Whether it's asking for a hug, making an offer of intimacy to a romantic partner, or just scheduling a massage … take an action step today. Then come back and make a few notes about how it went. How did the other person respond? How did it make you feel? Jot it all down right here.

_____
_____
_____
_____
_____

DAY 21: CHANGE YOUR HABITS, CHANGE YOUR EXPERIENCE

Here we are on the next-to-last day of this 22-day journey. If you've gotten this far with me, you've at least entertained the idea of change. I'm willing to bet that you've already implemented a lot of new actions, thoughts, and ideas in your life. I recognize you for that, and I'm very proud of what you've done. You see, it's all about showing up for yourself, taking new steps, and doing it with consistency. What you do consistently, of course, will be reflected in how life shows up for you.

That's why today I want to talk about habits. I mean the actions that you take every day on a regular basis that ultimately create your reality. If your life isn't quite showing up on the outside as often as you'd like it to, looking at your everyday habits might prove to be very illuminating.

The thing is, you might know that you want something different in your life. But you might be pushing your dreams away without your knowledge through self-sabotaging habits. Those habits could be anything, too. It could be something like always drinking that second glass of wine. It could be turning to drugs to alleviate pain. Maybe taking prescription drugs that make you feel lifeless. Perhaps it's pushing down emotions through eating. Or it might even be something a little more abstract, like perfectionism ... procrastination ... or unworthiness.

There are a lot of ways that you can derail your train. Today I'm going to show you ways to find those patterns of self-sabotage, break the habits that are associated with the patterns, and set yourself free.

You can identify the habits that keep you stuck, even if you've struggled to let it go in the past. You replace sabotaging habits with supportive ones, and it doesn't have to be like pulling teeth. I've managed to do it many times myself, and I know that you can do it too.

So today, I'm going to share with you some of the tools that you can use to recognize your day-to-day actions, and what is behind them. We'll talk about releasing the habits that get in your way ... and replacing them with practices that could set you free.

I've talked about my struggles with weight throughout this journey. I went from carrying extra weight in my teens to becoming exceptionally thin in my 20s. And if you recall, during those years I was always afraid of gaining every ounce back. But despite how much I fixated on what and how much I could eat, I began to recognize a curious pattern.

My afternoon routine back then focused on my young son. I'd pick him up from school, and then we'd work on his homework. We'd have dinner, and then he'd have a bath. We'd read a book, and then he'd be off to bed. It was all quality time spent with my kid. But it was what happened every night after he went to bed that caught my attention.

After my son was tucked in, I'd go sit down on the couch and "veg out" for the rest of the evening. Inevitably, snacks would enter the picture. Usually a LOT of snacks. Not just a small bowl of something. We're talking about a full bag of chips or a carton of ice cream. In one sitting.

So, there I would sit, watching whatever toxic programming was on my TV (including the news), unconsciously filling my body with crap. Sometimes until midnight or later, too.

Now, it wasn't that I wound up gaining a ton of weight. It was that I just didn't feel right. I had a hard time waking up in the morning. I was feeling lethargic rather than energized. It wasn't even so much the fact that I was eating "junk food" in large amounts, either. It was that I was eating unconsciously. I was taking in the energy of what was on TV automatically. I was staying up into the wee hours of the morning. Unconsciously. And it was starting to make me feel like absolute crap every morning.

I realized that these habits had created a monstrous pattern. It had been going on since my early teens, and it was in no way making my life better. How did I intend to stop staying up all night, ingesting negative vibes from both my food and my TV, and feeling like crap in the morning?

I decided that I had to do a complete overhaul of my routine and do it pronto.

I had to force my habits to change because I knew it wouldn't work for me any other way. So, what did I do? I didn't give myself the opportunity to be on the couch after my son went to bed. That meant tucking myself in just after I tucked my kid in for the night. Going to bed before I could plop down on the couch.

It wasn't easy, but I changed that well-ingrained habit. And I did it through a technique that is called "habit stacking." What does habit stacking entail, and what makes it unique?

Let's say that you have a habit that you want to change, but you know it's going to take a lot more than sheer willpower. You take a positive practice that you wish to create and add it onto something that you're already doing regularly. In this case, I decided that I wanted to stop taking a seat on the couch every night. I worked in the habit of getting up earlier by "stacking" my early bedtime on top of my son's regular bedtime.

It might not have been 100% easy-peasy, especially at first. But it worked.

Here's another example. Let's say that you know that your body benefits from a daily walk but getting out the door is like trying to corral a room full of cats. How can you establish that habit so that it becomes part of your daily routine instead of just something that you wished you could make yourself do? You add it to another daily non-negotiable task.

Maybe that task is taking the kids to school or driving home from work. You just "stack" the activity that you want to bring into your life on top of the daily imperative. So, every day after you drop the kids off at school, you go straight to the park for your walk. Or every day after you drive home from work, you grab your sneakers and power-walk around the neighborhood.

You create consistency by attaching something that you want to cultivate onto something else that is second-nature to you. It's a straightforward way to turn the "someday" items on your list into everyday practices.

Now, here's the thing: you do have a choice. You can decide to let a self-sabotaging habit go, or not. It's important to come from an intentional and inspirational place rather than shaming or threatening yourself into doing something that's "good" for you. It's about deciding that you want to feel better, more energized, and more peaceful. When you understand that changing your habits will make you feel the way you want to feel, "I HAVE to" becomes, "I GET to." That's what we're going for here.

"Get to" means "could." It means possibilities. "Have to" means "should." And automatic guilt. You have a choice. Which one sounds more exciting and empowering to you?

We all have habits that we'd rather not own up to, myself included. Today I want you to take some time to identify what those habits are. It's not because I want to point out where you're screwing up or ruining your life. All I'm asking you to do is bring awareness to the things you do every day. And from here decide which ones are supporting you, and which ones are sabotaging you.

Now, some people ask me what sabotage is, so let's clear that up before we go on. If you find yourself talking about a change that you want to make, but you don't follow through, that's just laziness, pure and simple. It may even be considered resistance, but it's not sabotage. Sabotage means that you start doing something, but you stop it for whatever reason. If you talk about going to the gym and getting ripped, but you never actually go, you're not sabotaging. But if you join a gym, show up like clockwork for a few days, but then abruptly stop and never go back, that's sabotage at its finest. These are the kind of habits that we're talking about.

So today, I'm asking you to identify the habits that are causing you guilt. What habits do you hide out of shame? Just bringing them out into the open begins the healing process, so do that first. Even if acknowledging them is all that you can do today, that's a start.

Let's say that you're a closet eater, for example. One of your new habits might be delegating the grocery shopping to someone else, so you're not tempted to throw "problem" foods into your cart. Another might be creating a shift in what you choose to eat. You might decide to bring vibrational awareness to your meals through a blessing or meditation. Maybe you feel that you eat too fast and it's causing you to miss out on the experience of your food. A new habit might be setting a timer, slowing down, and bringing focused attention to how you eat (rather than what you eat.)

Now, if you're like most of us and you have a habit you're not proud of, there's going to be some guilt and shame in the picture. The chances are that the guilt and shame have been there longer than you know. Remember that when you bring energy into your body, it has no choice but to respond. Would you prefer to bring in the power of love, support, and kindness rather than guilt, shame, and fear? I'm guessing that this is a "yes." Letting go of self-sabotaging, guilt-ridden habits is a beautiful place to start.

Where to begin? First of all, identify what it is that you want to release. Let's use a negative habit as an example, like smoking. Suppose that the very first thing you do when your feet hit the floor in the morning is reach for a cigarette. But what if you could take one small step in between getting up and lighting up? Maybe you could say a positive affirmation. Perhaps interject a brief meditation, or even just make yourself count to 100. Something small that comes between you and the activity you wish to release. That could be a single step in the right direction, and one that could set a foundation for the next step.

One of my habits upon waking is meditation. Then, I begin my gratitude practice. After that, I make myself a cup of tea and write in my gratitude journal. But there was a time that I didn't do any of these things. I had to create these habits, and I had to stack them on top of already existing practices. That is what got me creating habits that eventually became a loving and supportive routine.

Today you're going to identify one to three habits that you want to change, redirect, or release. I want you to be completely honest with yourself about how these practices are holding you back. Don't judge, just notice. What do you want to change, redirect, or release from your life, and what can you commit to so that it will happen? If you take the steps regularly, you'll see a change.

Different strategies work for different people. But start with discovering what habits are wreaking havoc and controlling your life. Maybe it's perfectionism, for example, and it shows up in your household. Perhaps you can't fall asleep until your entire house is tidy and complete, and your habit is staying up all night, trying to make everything perfect. Your first step might be making yourself go to bed and leave at least a little bit of a mess. This might help you to start the letting go of the things that are controlling you, even if it's just a first step.

That's the bottom line. Letting go of the things that are controlling you instead of supporting you. It's about loving yourself enough to stop sabotaging the things that you truly desire. And creating daily success habits that design the life you wish to create.

What's the Bottom Line?

- The actions that you take with consistency create your reality

- Habits and patterns can either support you or sabotage you

- The key is to find the habits that cause you guilt and shame

- Then replace these self-sabotaging habits with self-supporting habits

Practical Action Steps for Today...

Today, identify one to three habits that you know aren't serving you. Allow yourself to see where they came from, how you can shift them, and what step you can take today to begin healing them.

Maybe you've always been a perfectionist, and it is keeping you from taking action. You might spend a lot of time playing mindless phone games, and it's disrupting your sleep or affecting your relationships. Perhaps every time you decide to go to the gym, you let yourself get distracted by email or social media.

Some "mindless" habits are just for fun. But if it's obsessive or addictive, and it's taking away from the things that you value in life, it's worth considering.

Then, ask yourself what you could do to take that first step today. What can you commit to so that you'll start to release these actions that are holding you back?

Let's Write This! Questions to Ponder...

Part 1: What habits are keeping you stuck? Take a deep breath, relax, and start the exploration. What are one to three things that you want to ditch, once and for all? What would free up space in your life for more loving, productive, and kind rituals? Write them down right here.

_____

_____

_____

_____

_____

_____

_____

_____

_____

_____

Part 2: Where did they come from? Take a few moments and sit with these habits. Don't judge, don't push too hard. Simply ask yourself where they came from, why they've lasted so long, and if you're ready to let them go.

_____

_____

_____

_____

_____

_____

_____

_____

_____

Part 3: What can you commit to TODAY? Maybe it is taking a baby step in the direction of a more supportive alternative habit. Perhaps it's the "habit stacking" trick. For everything you want to dismiss, create an action step to move you in a new direction.

_____

_____

_____

_____

_____

_____

_____

_____

_____

DAY 22: BE AFFIRMATIVE. BE COMPLIMENTARY ... TO YOURSELF AND THE WORLD

You made it to Day 22! Congratulations and welcome. Welcome to the space that will change everything for you. You've grown, you've learned, and you've released. I hope that you see this moment for what it is: an invitation to continue the journey ... for your Mind, Body, and Spirit. Congratulate yourself on a job well done and take part in the excitement that the journey is just beginning for you!

I gave some serious consideration to how I wanted to bring this part of our journey to a close, as there are so many more exciting and enriching topics I could've chosen. But then I considered the recent passing of one of my biggest influences, Louise Hay. Her book "*You Can Heal Your Life*" was my first introduction to self-development, and it was a monumental experience. I decided that I wanted to end our time together with the topic that started my journey, a subject I discovered through the writings of Louise Hay: Affirmations and Compliments.

Now, I'm sure you've heard talk of "affirmations" for years. I bet you've used them in your own life, whether you did so formally or not. But what does "affirmation" mean, exactly? Is an affirmation necessarily a statement of kindness, love, or support? Maybe ... or maybe not. An affirmation is nothing more than a statement. It's neither negative nor positive, just something you state as truth. That means, like always, that you have a choice.

You can choose to affirm something loving and constructive. Or you can decide you'd rather declare something painful and destructive. Whether you know it or not, you're affirming things all the time. The key is to choose what you want to bring into your life and make your affirmations work for you, rather than against you.

How about compliments? They're expressions of appreciation and support. Maybe you have no problem expressing kindnesses to friends and strangers. But how about making a habit of extending those courtesies and kindnesses to yourself, too?

Today you're going to compliment yourself and do the same for the people in your life. After all, you don't lose any of your energy when you admire someone else. I believe that there is plenty for everyone. Happiness, joy, and fulfillment are available to ALL. I believe that we are here to affirm each other's value and worth, and an excellent place to start is by sincerely complimenting someone else.

How can you start using affirmations and compliments effectively every day? Maybe it starts with recognizing and loving your body. But it also might extend to include support, love and compliments to the rest of the world. Use this time not only to lift your vibration but do the same for everyone you meet.

I remember the day when I learned the mind-blowing truth that I shared with you above: I learned that affirmations aren't necessarily positive. They're merely statements. The effects of affirmations depend not on the words, but on the feelings behind the words. But I didn't know this when I was first introduced to the concept. Maybe that's why for so many years I believed that all that positive self-talk nonsense would never work for me.

I was 19 years old and had just had my first son when the book *"You Can Heal Your Life"* by Louise Hay landed in my lap. I couldn't even tell you exactly how I originally came across it. But I read most of it. I thought I understood it, but I didn't take it to heart just yet. I figured that positive self-talk sounded like a good idea, but who really believed it when they said it and how would that actually make a difference? I concluded that it just wasn't for me and put the book away.

Then six months later, I found myself sick and tired of being sick and tired. I was in pain – physically, mentally and emotionally. I had no clue how to resolve it. Then, through another miraculous coincidence, that same book came back into my consciousness. And this time I sincerely read it, all the way through.

This was when I finally understood that affirmations were just neutral statements. The thoughts, feelings, and emotions behind the words were what sealed the deal. What I also realized was that based on my experiences and environment, I was actually a master at affirmations. It's just that I was affirming everything that I DIDN'T want.

I affirmed the put-downs. I affirmed the fear. I affirmed the thoughts, feelings, and words of others that didn't feel good to me. I affirmed all kinds of fear and pain, and I'd been doing it perfectly for years.

Deciding to shift my focus and start affirming something else, however, proved to be a lot more challenging than I thought it would be. Day-by-day, moment-by-moment, I discovered nothing but life-defeating thoughts. And trying to change them was fucking hard. I know that is a strong word, but that is the only word to describe how hard it truly felt to actually do. It took time. It required painful awareness. There were times where I just gave up.

But every time I threw my hands up, I decided to give it another try. I kept hearing what Louise Hay said in her book: It won't feel real for a while. You might feel like you're making it up or lying to yourself. Keep affirming the positive anyway. Eventually, the energy will shift. You'll start thinking differently. You'll start feeling differently. Maybe not overnight, but soon. Perhaps even for the rest of your life, if you stay with it.

And I thought to myself, "Well, what I'm doing isn't working. So, what the hell, I'll give it a shot."

I won't say it was easy after that. It was painstaking work. I was exhausted and worn down by my thoughts up until then. Honestly, it was an uphill battle for a while. But I pushed and pushed. I didn't have anything else going for me. I might as well keep going and try to be loving and kind to myself. I mean, what's the worst thing that could happen? I'd end up back where I was.

I would tell myself things like, "You are a beautiful and loving person." Then I countered with, "That's not true." I would say, "You are wise." Then I'd turn right around and say, "Then why did you drop out of school at 15 years old?"

There was constant resistance. My environment at the time didn't help much, either. It was a low-vibrational space filled with negative, self-defeating people. Still, something in me knew that life was just not supposed to be this hard. There had to be a way of life that felt better than this. I didn't know what it was, but I had to believe that it was there.
So, in the midst of all the challenges, the pain, and the struggles, that tiny bit of hope kept me going. That's what pushed me to continue affirming what I wanted to be true, whether I believed that it was or not.

BODY REVIVAL WORKBOOK

You have to believe that there is a better way, no matter what evidence seems to be in front of you at the time. You may not have any proof of the positive possibilities, but you have a knowing, just as I did, that you are worthy of something better. You know that you deserve more. You know that there's got to be a way to release the pain so that it serves our highest good. You wouldn't be reading this right now if you'd given up all hope. You also probably suspect that the answers are within you, too.

I'm going to share a spoiler with you: you're right on all counts. Now, it's time to start affirming what you've always suspected to be true.

Now, here's the thing: it probably took a lot of time and repetition for the negative affirmations to become real. Don't be discouraged if it takes time for the positive ones to manifest into your reality. Be patient, be kind to yourself, and keep feeding the positive side. It's is a lot like the story of two wolves. Which one do you feed? Which one do you nurture? Because whichever one gets the attention is the one that will eventually win.

You ARE love, even though you might be feeling fear. You ARE abundant, even if you've been hung up on lack. It's just a matter of changing your focus. You simply need to get back to knowing who you truly are. You ARE love. You ARE worthy. It's time to start affirming that every day.

Today's topic is affirming and complimenting. Receiving compliments. And creating affirmations. Not only for yourself but everyone in your world.

Let's start by creating and using affirmations. Now, I'm not talking about just repeating something like, "I am worthy" or "I nourish my body with healthy food." I want you to focus on the *feelings* behind the words. You might feel like you're 'faking it till you make it' at first, and I get that. But focus on the emotions. The energy and the vibration behind the words is the real secret to affirmations.

Today you're going to create affirmations that you can believe in, even if you can't do it perfectly right away. You're going to choose the words that call forth your highest good. Focus on that expansive energy and run with it. And of course, allow yourself to receive the love and support that is coming your way.

Remember that what you focus on, expands. You can choose to affirm whatever you want. What if you could choose to affirm the peace, love, and light that is within you rather than the turmoil, fear, and darkness? I'm guessing that this sounds like a lot better of a deal.

Maybe affirmations won't turn your world around overnight. Just start where you are, right now. Choose to affirm more of what you want to see, and less of what you don't.

Then, decide to be complimentary to yourself and to others. Be the best friend that you can be to yourself, and you'll become a beacon for others, too. You deserve to be seen and recognized for who you are, and so does everyone else you meet.

What's the Bottom Line?

- Affirmations are neither positive or negative

- Whatever you decide to focus on is what becomes your reality

- Why not choose to focus on what you want to create?

- Positive affirmations might not feel real at first, and that's normal

- Keep saying them, focus on the feelings behind the words, and watch what happens

Practical Action Steps for Today...

Today I want you to think about what you want to create. Then start affirming it with all of your heart. Create an affirmation that is specific and unique to you. Focus on the feelings, and make your affirmation one that lights you up, even if you're not 100% convinced that it will come true. Yet. That's OK.

The key is in the feelings and the uniqueness. So, go wild! Make it exciting, inspiring, and motivating. Then start making it a part of your everyday life, starting today.

The second part is focusing on compliments. How can you uplift yourself today? In addition to your affirmation, come up with three things that you appreciate about yourself TODAY, as you are, right now. Then instead of simply stating your appreciation, turn it into a compliment that you give yourself. Say it to yourself like you would your best friend and allow yourself to receive it.

Then, take a moment today to give a sincere and heartfelt compliment to someone in your life. Your actual best friend, a co-worker, or the checkout clerk at the grocery store. Share a little bit of love and surprise someone by sharing your appreciation for THEM. You never know whose day you might make. Or even who's life you might change.

Let's Write This: Questions to Ponder...

Part 1: Create your new favorite affirmation. Focus on something that you want to bring to life. What do you want with all your heart? Write it down. Feel the feelings. Then create a present-tense affirmation and make it so. Choose one to three things that you want the most, then create a statement to start calling them in right now.

What I wish for the most right now is/are:

_____

_____

_____

_____

_____

_____

_____

_____

_____

_____

_____

_____

_____

_____

_____

My new favorite affirmation is/are:

_____

_____

_____

_____

_____

_____

_____

_____

_____

_____

Part 2: Compliments for everyone. What are your three appreciations for today? Write them down as a compliment to yourself and receive them as you would from a best friend. Then go out into the world, share the love, and give a heartfelt compliment to at least three people today.

The top three compliments I have for myself today are:

1._____

2._____

3._____

Who did YOU compliment today? How did they respond? Make a few notes here.

_____

_____

_____

_____

_____

_____

_____

_____

_____

_____

How can you make affirming and complimenting a part of YOUR daily life? How will you go forward after these 22 days with affirmations and compliments? Do a little brainstorming and journaling right here. Go wild, have fun, and get inspired. Then share the happiness with the world.

_____

_____

_____

_____

_____

_____

_____

_____

_____

_____

_____

_____

_____

_____

_____

_____

_____

_____

_____

_____

_____

_____

_____

_____

_____

_____

_____

CONCLUSION

WooHoo!!! You completed the 22 days of the Body Revival Workbook. If you are reading this, it means that you stuck with it. Awesome for you! It may have been really hard. Maybe you even stopped, and started and stopped again. Maybe you didn't invest as much energy as you would have liked, but you made it through. Remember, you can always do it again. Go deeper, be even more consistent. That is the wonderful thing. We are always learning and growing and expanding and each time, we peel another layer off, right?

My hope is that you gained a true BFF and some very valuable insight out of the Body Revival journey. Please, allow yourself to take the time to integrate all that you have become aware of, learned and expanded into. You may also see areas that you want to delve into even more, which is great. Like I say, if you are human, you probably have something to heal, expand or grow into awareness in.

Today, take a moment to give yourself a BIG HUG, from me. I so appreciate you and thank you for opening your heart and mind to some of the experiences in this book. It is my intention that you walk away lighter – in mind, body, spirit and emotions.

Love & Light,
Sunny Dawn Johnston

PS: If you would like to go even deeper, please check out my 22-Day Body Revival online course. It is filled with daily teaching videos, worksheets, downloads, and more. There is so much to this course to support your ongoing Body Revivalist adventure!
Check it out here: **https://soulfoodwithsunny.com/product/body-revival-course/**

ABOUT THE AUTHOR

Sunny Dawn Johnston is a world renowned author, inspirational speaker, spiritual teacher and psychic medium. Over the last eighteen years, Sunny has performed thousands of private sessions, readings and workshops which have helped people **connect with their heart** and **release the things that hold them back** from being their greatest version of themselves. Combining the *unconditional love* of a mother and the *tell-it-like-it-is honesty* of a best friend, Sunny helps people move into a higher vibration of living ... *and* a higher vibration of **Being**. Using her spiritual and intuitive gifts, she shines a light on the areas of lack, fear, insecurity and sometimes ... *B***S***!* Sunny feels strongly that at the heart of these issues is a lack of *Self-Love*. By reflecting the **true nature** of her clients back to them – **which *IS* Love** – they can experience, and then allow in that unconditional love, and begin to heal themselves.

Sunny is the author of over 20 books and has spoken worldwide on the subjects of *Intuition, Healing the Heart, Embracing the Body, Angels*, and *Self-Love*. Sunny has been featured internationally on numerous television and radio shows and has appeared in the award-winning documentary *Sacred Journey of the Heart*. She also starred in *"A Séance with..."* on Lifetime Movie Network (LMN).

She is the founder of **SOUL FOOD with SUNNY**, an Online Community for people of like minds and hearts to come together to expand, learn and heal. Sunny's latest online courses, *DETOX Your Life - A 44-Day Mind, Body, Spirit Detox; The Love Never Ends: Messages from the Other Side; and Body Revival* were released in 2017.

Sunny's latest endeavor, **SDJ Productions**, has expanded her beyond her writing and speaking events and into publishing and producing. She is the proud publisher of *365 Days of Angel Prayers* and the just recently released *111 Morning Meditations*.

Sunny is actively involved in the spiritual community and frequently conducts informational outreach work through a variety of organizations. She volunteers her time as a psychic investigator for the international organization FIND ME. This is a not-for-profit organization of Psychic, Investigative, and Canine Search & Rescue (SAR) volunteers working together to provide leads to law enforcement and families of missing persons and homicide.

In her spare time, you can find her enjoying time with family and friends. To learn more about Sunny's work, see videos and join in her community, please visit **www.sunnydawnjohnston.com** or **www.soulfoodwithsunny.com** and check out her Facebook page at **www.facebook.com/SunnyDawnJohnstonFanPage**.

OTHER BOOKS, PRODUCTS, AND SERVICES BY SUNNY DAWN JOHNSTON

Visit her online **Boutique** at
http://sunnydawnjohnstonboutique.com/

See a listing of her current in person and online **Classes** at
https://sunnydawnjohnston.com/calendar/

Get more information about her Soul Food with Sunny Community
www.soulfoodwithsunny.com

Private in-person or phone **Consultations** with Sunny can be scheduled at
http://sunnydawnjohnston.com/online-sunny-appointments/

View Sunny's custom designed **SDJewelry** at
http://sunnydawnjohnstonboutique.com/product-category/sdj-jewelry/

View Sunny's custom designed **Conscious Teez** clothing line at
http://sunnydawnjohnstonboutique.com/product-category/conscious-teez/

Sunny Dawn Johnston Books

Invoking the Archangels – A Nine-Step Process to Heal Your Body, Mind, and Soul

No one is truly alone. Every person can, at any moment, call upon not only one guardian angel, but also seven specific Archangels who bring blessings and protection to those who know how to ask. In *Invoking the Archangels: A Nine-Step Process to Healing Your Mind, Body, and Soul*, Sunny Dawn Johnston introduces readers to these Archangels and presents a nine-step process to healing on every level, from physical ailments to relationships, addiction and even financial struggles.

The Love Never Ends – Messages From The Other Side

Over the last fifteen years, Sunny Dawn Johnston has performed hundreds of readings for clients where she's communicated with spirits, guides, and their loved ones who have crossed over to the Other Side. The constant theme she receives from all of these divine entities and loved ones is this: Love never ends; fear exists only in this world.

In her new book *The Love Never Ends: Messages from the Other Side*, Sunny shares a selection of true and amazing stories from her experience as a psychic medium and intuitive. These encounters with the Other Side prove without a doubt that the universe is full of love.

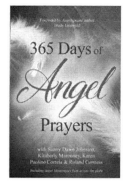

365 Days of Angel Prayers

What if every day you could encounter the divine? What if you could regularly know the blessing of deep peace and abiding joy? What if you could talk to angels? Great news—you can!

365 Days of Angel Prayers is a multi-author anthology of daily readings written to inspire and guide you to experience a rich and continuous communion with the angelic realm. Whether you choose to read that day's entry or take a more spirit-led approach, these prayers, blessings, invocations, and essays will help you learn how to communicate with angels. And as you allow the words to wash over your mind and heart, receiving the healing inherent within them, you will begin to see that there is no one way to pray for divine blessing or assistance. Soon, you may even find your own unique words pouring out—embrace them. Remember, this book is a collaboration, one you are warmly invited to join.

Soak in the deep peace, love, and joy of the angels. Through your daily connection, you will begin to shine their heavenly light and share their divine love with everyone you encounter.

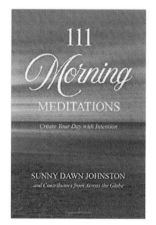

111 Morning Meditations – Create Your Day with Intention
A regular meditation habit can make you healthier, happier and more successful than ever!

What do history's greatest minds as well as today's most successful athletes, supermoms, CEOs and celebrities all have in common? They Meditate! Meditation is not just for the yogis. It's for everyone, of every age. Meditation is for all of humankind.

Thousands of years prove it, and Western science backs it up: Meditation removes stress and replaces it with a sense of inner peace and calm. It's one of the best tools you have to deal with physical and psychological distress, balance your emotions and be in the present moment. Meditation will help you experience greater calm in the midst of the chaos. It will connect you to your inner-most feelings and challenge our habits of self-judgment.

From the creator of *365 Days of Angel Prayers* comes a new book on how meditation can help you lower blood pressure, relieve chronic pain, reduce stress and celebrate life. *111 Morning Meditations - Create your Day with Intention* offers you the opportunity to start your day with peace and tranquility, helping you create a habit that can only benefit you and those around you. Meditation opens the door to real happiness, health and healing.

No Mistakes! How You Can Change Adversity into Abundance
Have you ever wondered if there was any truth to the adage, "Everything happens for a reason"? Wonder no more. This is the book that demonstrates the truth in that old piece of conventional wisdom. Madisyn Taylor, Sunny Dawn Johnston, Heather Ash and twenty other motivational and inspirational authors and speakers explore how synchronicities, blessings, and miracles can be found even in the most seemingly daunting circumstances.

Written from the perspective that every experience that you have is designed to be an opportunity for growth, *No Mistakes* contains over twenty-five uplifting chapters, each contributed by a different author. Each story demonstrates how what appear to be dire circumstances are ultimately opportunity for blessings. Drawing on situations ranging from financial hardship, divorce, and even death of a loved one, these accounts leave no doubt that even in the darkest moments of our lives, a divine hand is at work. For anyone traveling a rough road or experiencing difficulties, this will provide the fortitude to move ahead. There is indeed a silver lining behind every dark cloud.

Living Your Purpose with Sunny Dawn Johnston & Friends
What is my purpose? What am I meant to do, who am I meant to be? What do I need to do to serve my purpose? MY purpose, YOUR purpose, and/or OUR purpose is to simply just BE … To BE, in whatever form that is for you. *Living Your Purpose* illustrates how the focus is constantly changing as we grow and evolve; and therefore the form purpose takes in your life, is ever changing.

The Wedding Officiant's Manual: A Guide to Writing, Planning and Officiating Wedding Ceremonies

The Wedding Officiant's Manual is an essential guide for anyone who wants to create a wedding ceremony. Sunny Dawn Johnston, an Ordained Officiant with over a decade of experience, has written this book from the Officiants perspective. However, this manual can be used by brides, grooms and wedding consultants as well as ceremony Officiants.

Archangel Michael: Maintain Your Energy: A 33-Day Guidebook

The *Archangel Michael: Maintain your Energy 33-Day Guidebook* will help you to develop a direct and consistent connection with this powerful Archangel. Archangel Michael is the Archangel of protection, guidance, strength and courage. Learning to invite him into your life will help you to maintain your energy. If you are a sensitive person – picking up everyone's energy, struggling to separate your "stuff" from their "stuff," feeling responsible to fix everyone and everything – this book will change your life. This 33-Day Guidebook is designed to help you create a committed relationship with Archangel Michael. It will help you to learn how to invoke his presence in your daily life, discern his loving protective energy and feel his presence and strength. Most importantly ... this guidebook will help you learn to become an observer of other people's energy instead of an absorber of other people's energy. With a 33-day commitment to yourself and Archangel Michael, you will find energy and awareness that you never knew. Start today and open up to a whole new magical world with Archangel Michael. When you invoke the Archangels, they are there immediately, regardless of what your physical senses may observe. Trust that when you ask, it is given; and when you invoke, they are present.

Archangel Raphael: Healing & Restoration: A 33-Day Guidebook

The *Archangel Raphael: Healing and Restoration 33-Day Guidebook* will help you to develop a direct and consistent connection with this powerful Archangel. Archangel Raphael is the Archangel of Healing and Restoration – physically, mentally, emotionally, spiritually and energetically. Learning to invite him into your life will help you to heal: Mind, Body and Soul. If you are someone that struggles to maintain wellness, this book and the techniques within it can absolutely change your life.

This 33-Day Guidebook is designed to help you create a committed relationship with Archangel Raphael. It will help you to learn how to invoke his presence in your daily life, discern his healing energy and feel his support and strength. Most importantly, this guidebook will help you learn to recognize the power you have to ask for healing ... and more importantly, to love yourself enough to allow yourself to receive it. With a 33-day commitment to yourself and Archangel Raphael, you will find that healing energy is your natural birthright. We are meant to be well. Start today and open up to a whole new magical world with Archangel Raphael. When you invoke the Archangels, they are there immediately, regardless of what your physical senses may observe. Trust that when you ask, it is given; and when you invoke, they are present.

Healing Mandalas Coloring Book Paperback

Mandalas are ancient symbols of wisdom, guidance, and spiritual connection. Healing Mandalas Coloring Book allows you to relax with these sacred circles finding peace, inspiration, and a new form of expression and connection to both the internal and external worlds. Best-selling Author, Sunny Dawn Johnston, in collaboration with Artist Lori Farrell, has created *Healing Mandalas Coloring Book* to support YOU in your healing process through these ancient symbols. The mandala is a symbol of the self, and in coloring one, it offers a connection and expression to our innermost thoughts and feelings. You can use these sacred circles as a meditative practice, a healing exercise in times of pain or crisis, an expression of feelings and emotions and, of course, the simple act of creativity. Featuring 30 unique and inspirational mandala drawings, this book encourages you to use your imagination to create vibrant patterns that help you to release any pain – physical, mental or emotional – and allow more joy, happiness and peace into your life ... bringing you closer to your true self. Each intricate design will draw your eye inward, shifting your focus toward your center and allowing you to fully relax your mind as you express yourself through these healing mandalas. Complete with expert instruction and design tips, the *Healing Mandala Coloring Book* will help you find your inner calm and creativity every day. Adults of all ages will enjoy this special coloring book designed to let go of the worries, fears, and concerns and let the healing begin.

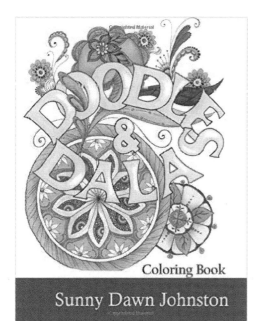

Doodles and Dalas Coloring Book Paperback

Featuring 40 unique and inspirational original Doodle and Mandala drawings, this book encourages you to use your imagination to create vibrant patterns that help you to release any pain – physical, mental or emotional – and allow more joy, happiness and peace into your life … bringing you closer to your true self. Coloring has been proven to calm anxiety and depression. Each intricate design will draw your eye inward, shifting your focus toward your center and allowing you to fully relax your mind as you express yourself through these healing mandalas and doodles. Complete with expert instruction and design tips, the *Doodles and Dalas Coloring Book* will help you find your inner calm and creativity every day. Adults of all ages, and even older children, will enjoy this special coloring book designed to let go of the worries, fears, and concerns and let the healing begin. A Doodle is a simple drawing that can have real meaning, or may just be abstract shapes. Dalas (Mandalas) are ancient symbols of wisdom, guidance, and spiritual connection. Best-selling Author, Sunny Dawn Johnston, in collaboration with Artists Staci Mitchell Randall and Lori Farrell, has released her second creatively-inspired Coloring Book: Doodles and Dalas. Printed on 8.5" x 11" high quality paper, you'll have plenty of space to express your creativity.

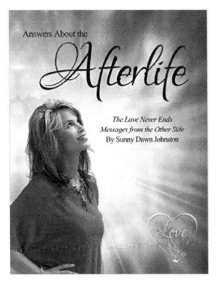

Answers About the Afterlife

The topic of the Afterlife is one of absolute extremes that most people have an opinion about.

As a Psychic Medium with over 30 years of experience, I am answering these questions based on my own personal experience with the Afterlife. Years of questions that my clients, friends, and students have asked me, and their loved ones in Spirit, throughout the years. These answers are in no particular order and were usually asked in response to this question:

If you could have one question answered about death or what happens during or after you die, what would it be?

The answers within this book are from my own personal experience and observation. They are based on communication, interpretation and conversation I've had over the years with the Spirit world. My intention in sharing them with you is not to say this is the right way, but to simply answer common questions based on MY experience.

The questions are grouped by topic. Some answers are more detailed than others. For many of these topics, it is most helpful to read all responses in a particular section to get an overall feel for my answer.

Invoking the Archangels Workbook: A 9-Step Process to Heal Your Body, Mind and Soul Paperback

Invoking the Archangel Workbook is designed to help you connect with the Archangels through a variety of hands on experiential exercises. This workbook teaches you how to work with the Archangels to help you heal your body, mind and soul. Whether you are in need of healing, forgiveness, protection, self-love or simply want to create a stronger connection with your angels, this workbook and the Nine Step Process will help you create that connection with your Angels and ultimately, heal your heart. This workbook can be used as a standalone or as a companion to Sunny Dawn Johnston's best-selling book, *Invoking the Archangels A Nine-Step Process to Heal Your Body, Mind, and Soul.*

Sunny Dawn Johnston CDs

Invoking the Archangels - To Heal Mind, Body and Soul
Heal your mind, body and soul by invoking the support of the Archangels. In this CD, Sunny introduces you to the 7 Archangels and teaches you how to invite them into your daily life for Protection (Michael), Communication (Gabriel), Healing (Raphael), Wisdom (Uriel), Unconditional Love (Chamuel), Beauty (Jophiel) and Forgiveness (Zadkiel). Sunny also offers you a guided meditation to experience the Archangels and your own Guardian Angel for yourself.

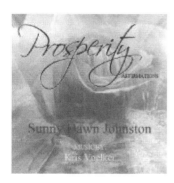

Prosperity Affirmations
Developing a positive mindset is one of the most powerful life strategies there is. Using powerful positive thinking techniques, visualizations and prosperity affirmations, it is possible to achieve whatever you want. In this CD, Sunny and her musician **Kris Voelker**, team up to bring you an audio experience that offers words of wisdom and vibrational music that will permeate your consciousness and fill you with hope and inspiration.

Positive Affirmations
Developing a positive mindset is one of the most powerful life strategies there is. Using powerful positive thinking techniques, visualizations and positive affirmations, it is possible to achieve whatever you want. In this CD, Sunny and her musician **Kris Voelker**, team up to bring you an audio experience that offers words of wisdom and vibrational music that will permeate your consciousness and fill you with hope and inspiration. You can start your day off with a gentle, meditative, relaxed journey; or an energetic beat that moves your Spirit to these positive affirmations.

Soul Transitions - A Medium's Journey to the Spirit World

In this CD, Sunny shares her experiences as a psychic medium and teaches you how to use your own natural abilities to connect with deceased loved ones and the Spirit World. She will help you understand the ways in which your deceased loved ones communicate with you, which is often through signs and symbols that are sometimes missed. She will also provide you with tools to continue your communication with the spirit world.

Sunny begins the CD by discussing the final stages of a soul's physical existence and offers insights into what happens when a soul leaves the body. She will share and teach from a medium's point of view, as well as from her own personal experiences as a granddaughter and a friend. Sunny continues the CD by teaching you how to connect with your own deceased loved ones, identify your psychic and spiritual gifts, and how to discern the energies of the deceased people around you.

Sunny's teaching is complimented by a guided mediation that will help you connect with your own deceased loved ones. This connection will help you to share any messages you may have and to listen to what your deceased loved ones might want to share with you.

To complete the journey, Soul Musician **Kris Voelker**, includes two beautiful songs that connect you to your loved ones and allow you to heal through any grief you may still be feeling from this transition process.

Embracing the Body That Is - A Guide to Loving Yourself

This CD contains the personal story of how Sunny learned to love, accept and appreciate her body. Throughout her life, Sunny struggled with her weight, self-esteem, and loving herself. She had a terrible body image, and her body reflected this belief. Sunny's story reveals what she did to end her self-sabotage, negative self-talk and pain. If you have struggled with body image issues and self-acceptance, then this CD is for you. Sunny not only offers her own story, but includes affirmations and a meditation to help you to connect to the sources of strength and healing within yourself. Sunny Dawn Johnston is a widely known and respected International Psychic Medium and Spiritual Teacher. As a national speaker, Sunny's dynamic methods effectively reach out to help people to help themselves by discovering that the answers are always within.

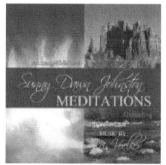

Grounding and Archangel Michael Meditation

Guided meditation is for anyone who would like to experience deep relaxation and inner peace by harnessing the power of your mind. By simply listening to these guided meditations, it's never been easier to eliminate stress and experience a deeply satisfying state of mind. Sunny, and her musician **Kris Voelker,** teamed up to bring you this meditation CD.

Grounding Meditation – Sunny's voice guides you through a grounding meditation that you may use either as an addition to your current spiritual practice, or as the basis for starting one. Soothing ambient music serves as the backdrop for this guided journey that includes a full-body relaxation, as well as steps for energetically connecting with the planet, the heavens, the five elements, and aligning with one's own Divinity.

Archangel Michael – Sunny's voice, and the soothing music of soul musician **Kris Voelker,** guides you through a meditation to connect you with Archangel Michael. Call on Archangel Michael when you need protection, courage or strength. If you've had a stressful or negative experience that is causing you physical or emotional pain, it's wonderful to call on Archangel Michael, who is the supreme helper in releasing fear. He is also the "one" to call in to protect yourself from absorbing negative energy or experiences. Learn how to invoke his loving protective energy into your life today through this step-by-step guided meditation.

Conversations with Sunny

I'd like to invite you to sit down and join me in a conversation that was recorded in front of a live audience for the purpose of this CD on the topics which include Body Image, Manifestation and Self Worth. Listen in on the conversations that could hold some of the guidance and support that you are looking for at this time. There is a wide variety of information that may also serve family or friends! Through this CD, anyone can put themselves in a chair sitting across from Sunny, and receive some guidance and direction just by listening to the conversation, hearing your own questions and answers, and allowing Spirit to guide you back to the answers that are already within you!

Healing Your Grief: Affirmations of Hope

On this MP3 album download, Sunny offers affirmations from various authors to help move you thru the grief stage and provide a different perspective on loss. Soul musician **Kris Voelker** has added the music to help support the vibration of these messages and help support someone who is in active grief or facing an upcoming loss. This album will be made into a physical CD soon as well.

Made in the USA
San Bernardino, CA
04 January 2018